THERAPEUTIC COMMUNITY

THERAPEUTIC COMMUNITY

HELD AT

MANHATTAN STATE HOSPITAL
WARD'S ISLAND, NEW YORK

Compiled and Edited by

HERMAN C. B. DENBER, M. D.

Director of Psychiatric Research, Manhattan State Hospital

Ward's Island, New York

Instructor in Psychiatry, College of Physicians and Surgeons

Columbia University

New York

CHARLES C THOMAS · PUBLISHER

Springfield · Illinois · U.S.A.

CHARLES C THOMAS • PUBLISHER

BANNERSTONE HOUSE

301-327 East Lawrence Avenue, Springfield, Illinois, U.S.A.

Published simultaneously in the British Commonwealth of Nations by

BLACKWELL SCIENTIFIC PUBLICATIONS, LTD., OXFORD, ENGLAND

Published simultaneously in Canada by

THE RYERSON PRESS, TORONTO

Library of Congress Catalog Card Number: 59-14193

With THOMAS BOOKS careful attention is given to all details of manufacturing and design. It is the Publisher's desire to present books that are satisfactory as to their physical qualities and artistic possibilities and appropriate for their particular use. THOMAS BOOKS will be true to those laws of quality that assure a good name and good will.

Printed in the United States of America

PARTICIPANTS

DR. THOMAS J. BOAG: *Assistant to Director*, Allan Memorial Institute of Psychiatry, Montreal, Canada.

DR. JEAN B. BOULANGER: *Assistant Professor of Psychiatry*, Faculty of Medicine, University of Montreal; Hôpital Notre-Dame, Montreal, Canada.

DR. HENRY BRILL: *Assistant Commissioner*, Department of Mental Hygiene, Albany, New York.

DR. GEORGE W. BROOKS: *Director of Research and Staff Education*, Vermont State Hospital, Waterbury, Vermont.

DR. DEXTER M. BULLARD, JR.: *Resident Psychiatrist*, Massachusetts Mental Health Center, Boston, Massachusetts.

DR. RUPERT A. CHITTICK: *Superintendent*, Vermont State Hospital, Waterbury, Vermont.

DR. TRAVIS E. DANCY: *Psychiatrist-in-Chief*, Queen Mary Veterans Hospital; *Associate Professor of Psychiatry*, Faculty of Medicine, McGill University, Montreal, Canada.

DR. WILLIAM N. DEANE: *Sociologist*, Vermont State Hospital, Waterbury, Vermont.

DR. HERMAN C. B. DENBER: *Director of Psychiatric Research*, Manhattan State Hospital, Ward's Island, New York, New York; *Instructor in Psychiatry*, College of Physicians and Surgeons, Columbia University, New York, New York.

DR. PIERRE DENIKER: *Physician*, Psychiatric Hospitals of Paris; Department of Psychiatry (Clinique St. Anne), Faculty of Medicine, University of Paris, France.

DR. MAURICE DESPINOY: *Director*, Hôpital Psychiatrique, Départment de la Martinique, West Indies.

MRS. ANNE EVANS: *Psychiatric Social Worker*, Massachusetts Mental Health Center, Boston, Massachusetts.

v

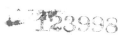

DR. MAX FINK: *Director of Research*, Department of Experimental Psychiatry, Hillside Hospital, Glen Oaks, New York.

DR. JACK FREUND: *Director of Clinical Research*, A. H. Robins Company, Inc., Richmond, Virginia.

DR. FRITZ A. FREYHAN: *Clinical Director and Director of Research*, Delaware State Hospital, Farnhurst, Delaware; *Assistant Professor of Psychiatry*, University of Pennsylvania, Philadelphia, Pennsylvania.

DR. ALEXANDER GRALNICK: *Director*, High Point Hospital, Port Chester, New York; *Associate Clinical Professor of Psychiatry*, New York Medical College, New York, New York.

DR. HARRY GRAUER: *Research Fellow in Psychiatry*, Queen Mary Veterans Hospital, Montreal, Canada.

DR. MILTON GREENBLATT: *Assistant Superintendent and Director of Research and Laboratories*, Massachusetts Mental Health Center, Boston, Massachusetts.

DR. FRIEDA R. HENDELES: *Senior Psychiatrist and Director of Social Therapy*, Delaware State Hospital, Farnhurst, Delaware.

DR. PAUL H. HOCH: *Commissioner*, Department of Mental Hygiene, Albany, New York.

MISS BARBARA R. HOFFMAN: *Social Psychologist*, Massachusets Mental Health Center, Boston, Massachusetts.

DR. ANTHONY HORDERN: *Visiting Scientist*, St. Elizabeths Hospital, Washington, D. C.

DR. SAMUEL IRWIN: *Section Head*, Pharmacology, Schering Corporation, Bloomfield, New Jersey.

DR. MARTIN M. KATZ: *Executive Secretary*, Psychopharmacology Review Committee, Psychopharmacology Service Center, National Institute of Mental Health, Bethesda, Maryland.

MISS DOROTHY KAUFFMAN, R. N.: *Head Nurse*, Manhattan State Hospital, Ward's Island, New York, New York.

DR. ISRAEL KESSELBRENNER: *Supervising Psychiatrist*, Manhattan State Hospital, Ward's Island, New York, New York.

MR. WILLIAM E. KIRSCH: *Research Associate*, Smith, Kline & French Laboratories, Philadelphia, Pennsylvania.

DR. GERALD L. KLERMAN: *Chief of Service*, Massachusetts Mental Health Center, Boston, Massachusetts.

DR. ELSIE B. KRIS: *Principal Research Scientist (Social Psychiatry)*, Manhattan Aftercare Clinic, New York, New York.

DR. SIMON KWALWASSER: *Associate Medical Director*, Hillside Hospital, Glen Oaks, New York.

DR. H. PETER LAQUEUR: *Supervising Psychiatrist*, Creedmoor State Hospital, Queens Village, New York.

DR. DANIEL J. LEVINSON: *Director*, Center for Socio-psychological Studies, Massachusetts Mental Health Center, Boston, Massachusetts.

DR. DON R. LIPSITT: *Research Assistant*, Clinical Psychiatry Section, St. Elizabeths Hospital, Washington, D. C.

DR. ANTHONY F. MESZAROS: *Psychiatrist*, Ste. Anne's Hospital, Ste. Anne de Bellevue, Quebec, Canada.

DR. KENNETH B. MOORE: *Clinical Director*, Ypsilanti State Hospital, Ypsilanti, Michigan.

DR. WILLIAM A. OGLE: *Clinical Demonstrator—Psychiatry*, King County Hospital, Seattle, Washington.

MRS. GERALDINE OSBORNE, R. N.: *Supervisor*, Social Therapeutic Program, Delaware State Hospital, Farnhurst, Delaware.

DR. PAUL RAJOTTE: *Resident*, Manhattan State Hospital, Ward's Island, New York, New York.

DR. MAX RINKEL: *Research Associate*, Massachusetts Mental Health Center, Boston, Massachusetts.

DR. LEIGH M. ROBERTS: *Assisant Professor of Psychiatry*, University Hospitals of Wisconsin, Madison, Wisconsin.

DR. GERALD J. SARWER-FONER: *Consultant in Psychiatry and Director of Psychiatric Research*, Queen Mary Veterans Hospital, Montreal, Canada.

DR. C. CONWAY SMITH: *Consultant*, Department of Veterans Affairs, Montreal, Canada.

MR. MARK SPIVAK: *Research Social Psychologist*, Ypsilanti State Hospital, Ypsilanti, Michigan.

DR. RICHARD F. TISLOW: *Chief Pharmacologist*, Wyeth Institute for Medical Research, Radorn, Pennsylvania.

DR. JOHN H. TRAVIS: *Director*, Manhattan State Hospital, Ward's Island, New York, New York.

"Research Conference on Therapeutic Community"
Manhattan State Hospital, Ward's Island, New York
March 13, 14, 15, 1959.

PREFACE

The following proceedings describe the different aspects of the so-called therapeutic community in a mental hospital setting. At this time the organization of mental hospitals is in a state of flux. Many more aspects of mentally ill patient care must be taken into consideration than was formerly the case. The open-door policy, the introduction of effective therapeutic agents such as the tranquilizing drugs, the different community relations in connection with the hospital, and the establishment of patient governments in many places all point toward new and interesting concepts in hospital management. Through experimentation we will have to determine how many of these ideas are not only new but also valuable, how many we will have to discard, and how many we will have to fuse with older ideas of hospital management. We are sure that everyone reading this book will be impressed by the many constructive thoughts expressed and how, with different approaches to the same problem, an integrated treatment of the patient can be evolved.

Paul H. Hoch, M.D.

FOREWORD

The papers in this volume were read at a meeting held in Manhattan State Hospital, March 13-15, 1959, with Henry Brill, M. D., Assistant Commissioner of Mental Hygiene, Albany, N. Y., as chairman. This was the second reunion of the group, whose Montreal discussions are chronicled in *The Dynamics of Psychiatric Drug Therapy* (ed., G. J. Sarwer-Foner, M. D., Springfield, Illinois, Charles C Thomas, Publisher).

The general movement to open mental hospitals, intensify treatment, and rehabilitate the chronically ill is a relatively recent event, although it has waxed and waned during the past 100 years. The advent of many new chemotherapeutic agents since 1952, with their striking effects and the intensive research program that resulted, have once again renewed interest in the "total" treatment process. With a constant accrual of patients and increasing size of hospitals, this new approach became a necessity with the eventual hope of reversing the previous trend.

It would be fruitless to debate the primary or relative importance of a chemical, psychological, sociological or physiological treatment of the psychoses or, for that matter, the neuroses. Life processes show a complex series of interaction patterns with interdependence of organ systems, that are in turn dependent on external stimuli. Such a concept only allows for an integrated approach. Whatever the social structure may be, large or small, it is difficult to separate out any one variable without influencing innumerable other factors.

This group had previously discussed the psychoanalytic aspects of drug therapy and many new areas for study were brought forward. Drugs were being prescribed in a social setting in which a reciprocal relationship existed between treatment and milieu, apart from the production of purely chemical and physiological effects. It was felt that the medical and nursing staffs must become aware of their role in the treatment process over and above the actual carrying out of each procedure. Only by integrating all therapeutic endeavors would the patient be able to secure maximum gain.

Study of the therapeutic community, whether in a state hospital, university clinic or elsewhere, offers an unparalleled opportunity to observe the intricacies of abnormal human behavior as affected by a) changes in the social field, b) staff interpersonal relations, c) drug or other therapies, and finally, the interaction of each with the other.

THE EDITOR

ACKNOWLEDGMENTS

Grateful acknowledgment is made to John H. Travis, M. D., Director, and Mr. Dennis J. O'Shea, Business Officer, for their excellent cooperation and arrangements for the meeting. Mrs. Emma A. Rothblatt, Deputy Commissioner, Department of Commerce and Public Events of the City of New York, gave much help in facilitating special functions. Miss Selma Sterrn, secretary for the Research Division, spent long hours and gave unstintingly of her time in preparation of the manuscript and correction of galley proofs. The A. H. Robins Company, Inc., Schering Corporation, Smith, Kline & French Laboratories, and Wyeth Laboratories aided in support for the meeting.

H. C. B. D.

CONTENTS

THERAPEUTIC COMMUNITY

HISTORICAL BACKGROUND
OF THE THERAPEUTIC COMMUNITY

Henry Brill, M. D.

3

THE NEED FOR A HISTORICAL REVUE

The mental hospital in its modern form is about 150 years old and its history for much of that period resembles that of Mark Twain's alcoholic who was always being reformed with much pomp and ceremony and then quietly relapsing to offer someone else the pleasure of reforming him again. The hospital story opens with the reforms of such men as Chiarugi, Pinel and Tuke; it is carried on through the mid-nineteenth century by such names as Conolly, Dix and Kirkbride, and moves into the present era with Weir, Mitchell, Beard and many more. In essence, their campaigns can be seen as efforts to change the hospitals into truly therapeutic communities. They brought under attack such anti-therapeutic characteristics as authoritarianism, rigidity, isolation, poor communication and lack of progress as well as downright brutality. They repeatedly set up programs of liberalization, humanization, education of the public, therapeutic hope for the patient and restoration of his human rights and equality with other citizens. Yet, in general, these improvements were subsequently engulfed by new periods of overcrowding, understaffing, underfinancing and their corollaries, dirt, brutality and the traditional "madhouse" atmosphere, all of which were not improved by first renaming the institutions "asylums" and then "mental hospitals."

Today we are again caught up in a reform movement which seeks to redesign the social-psychiatric structure of the hospitals under the new names of "therapeutic community" and the "open hospital," yet in essence the purpose and much of the method are not far removed from the reforms of the past; psychiatry has passed this way several times before and has lost the road each time. Why did this happen and what hopes do we have that this time we may retain our hard won gains, not to speak of advancing further? Earl Bond struck a pessimistic note on this topic when he wrote (1) in 1947 that the successes of Dorothea Linde Dix ". . . are almost unbelievable, and it is nearly as incredible that the work she did has to be done all over again. . . . It is not pleasant to notice that advances in science remain with us while advancement in humanity melts away over night."

Let us keep this statement in mind as we review the historical background of the therapeutic community.

MAXWELL JONES AND THE BRITISH EXPERIMENT

While the basic concepts have a long history, the term "therapeutic community" in its present sense is new and first came to be generally known in relation to the work in Britain of Maxwell Jones (2) who used it to describe a hospital organization and a treatment regime for a group of unemployable persons suffering from neuroses and character disorders. Beginning in World War II with a "neurosis unit," which emphasized sociological and psychological concepts in the treatment of "effort syndrome," Jones carried these ideas over into a hospital unit for the treatment of ex-prisoners of war and then further elaborated the method in the Industrial Neurosis Unit at Belmont Hospital beginning in 1947. As one studies his method, the following salient points emerge (and these should be compared with the Borstal system discussed below):

1. That it is oriented to productive work and quick return to society. It is considered a form of social psychiatry and the book is "published in England under the title of *Social Psychiatry*" (2).

2. Educational techniques play an important role in reorienting the patients and there is liberal use at the same time of group dynamics and group pressures for constructive purposes. The attitude seems to be that for some purposes groups can be treated more effectively than individuals.

3. A marked diffusion of authority to personnel and to patients is a key characteristic of the system. The operation is strongly democratic and represents a flight from authoritarianism.

THE THERAPEUTIC COMMUNITY AND A BROADER SOCIAL PSYCHIATRY

The organization began as a bold effort to solve the problem of a vast volume of psychiatric work with limited facilities and to treat a group of individuals who had previously been considered untreatable in the psychiatric sense. However, as stated in the

6

"Foreword" to the book (2), it has implications for "the design of a whole culture which will foster healthy personalities," and "the carefully managed relationships within . . . an institution" are seen as a contribution to a future "psychosanitation" by which social psychiatrists "will normally protect entire communities from ways of life that are emotionally crippling."

The cover of this book announces the Therapeutic Community as a "New Treatment Method in Psychiatry" and indeed there is much that is new in the technique and procedure and especially in its application to acting out character disorders; nevertheless it does have well marked antecedents.

EARLY CONCEPTS OF "THERAPEUTIC COMMUNITY" UNDER OTHER NAMES

The broad aim so clearly expressed in the "Foreword" is as old as the idea that man is the product of his environment and that the creation of a more perfect environment will produce a more perfect man. Plato's *Republic* (3) is an early attempt to design such a society and the very words he uses remind one of those of the "Foreword." "When any of the citizens experiences good or evil the whole state will make his case their own—rejoice or sorrow with him." . . . "And is not that the best ordered state which most nearly approaches to the condition of the individual; as in the body, when but a finger of one of us is hurt, the whole frame . . . feels the hurt and sympathizes all together with the part affected . . ."

The *Republic* was the first of a long series of books on the production of an earthly paradise; among others are *Utopia* by Sir Thomas Moore (1516), *New Atlantis* by Francis Bacon (1624), and more modern works, such as Butler's *Erehwon* and Wells' *A Modern Utopia*. Nor did interest cease at the theoretical level. Such efforts as the Oneida Community and Mormonism were attempts to implement the theory of the more perfect environment and to apply directly the principles of group action, individual freedom, democratic self-government, and the value of productive work. They also included community of property and wives which has now lost popularity. In addition, Plato's ideas have had

7

much influence on subsequent social thinking and planning. Plato also apparently had some awareness of the mental hygiene aspects of social harmony. He writes, "Wrongness of form and . . . the lack of harmony are . . . fraternal to wrongness of mind and character."

The similarity of the broad orientation of certain workers in social psychiatry to that of Plato's *Republic* appears from a parallel reading of passages from both sources. For example, a modern writer says (4), "I believe that 'mental health' is an emerging goal and a value for humanity of a kind comparable to the notions of 'finding God,' 'salvation,' 'perfection' or 'progress.'"

Plato seems to use the word "just" in the same enveloping sense. "The aim of the state is not to make the citizens happy. It is to make the state, and by the same token the individual, just. . . . The just state and the just man are the happiest."

Says one commentator, "Before the great myth at the end of the *Republic* is concluded, Plato leaves no uncertain implication that the just state is indeed the happiest and thus, too, with the just man."

EARLY MOVES TOWARD THERAPEUTIC COMMUNITIES IN MENTAL HOSPITALS

It may be going very far afield to digress into Greek philosophy in a discussion of the therapeutic community in modern mental hospitals, yet it seems worthwhile to establish the fact that fundamentals of the idea are old, perhaps as old as mankind. Let us now see where, in mental hospitals, similar formulations have been applied in the past and what the results have been. If we find that they have had a uniform history of failure, we can still be optimistic about the outlook of the present movement if we find that some essential operating conditions have changed and thus offer a more favorable surrounding for the type of organization we now call the "therapeutic community."

The mental hospital history opens with the "Moral Treatment" of Pinel. Preceded by Chiarugi and Daquin and followed by Tuke, Pinel brought to mental hospital patients the Liberty,

8

Equality and Fraternity promised to all by the French Revolution. In their "Moral Treatment" one already finds the essential outlines of a total hospital organization for therapeutic purposes, the use of occupation, recreation, instruction, stress on kindness and patience, the avoidance of the use of constraint and force, and the support of human dignity even in such minor matters as calling the patients "guests." A re-reading of some of the original writings shows this system of therapy quite in line with our most recent thinking although many items are absent, some because they were carried under a different name or simply in the name of humanity or common sense. Only the more formal aspects of group and individual psychotherapy and of patient government are entirely lacking in addition to the technical and scientific developments of diagnosis and therapy of the last 150 years.

In mid-century we find another group of reforms and reformers working under a different terminology but still fighting much the same battle. Conolly is chiefly known to us for the word "non-restraint" but he says (7), "The mere abolition of fetters and restraints constitutes only a part of what is properly called 'the non-restraint system.' Accepted in its true and full sense it is a complete system of management of insane patients of which the operation begins the moment a patient is admitted over the threshold of an asylum." Closer examination indicates that his "whole system" was not far different from that of the "moral therapy" which went before and has much in common with much that has followed. He, too, had in mind a type of therapeutic community. His Hanwell Asylum still exists, though under another name; it is one of the largest in England, but there is reason to believe that Conolly's influence did not long outlive him even at Hanwell. Elsewhere, the effects of his work, like those of Dorothea Linde Dix in the United States, were swallowed up in the rising tide of mental hospital cases which swamped all facilities. In the last half of the century we again find in America a recurrence of the bitterest criticisms and suspicions of the hospitals. Nor were attacks always evidence of serious malfeasance and mishandling of the mentally ill. Rather, they had become part of an American tradition of attack on mental hospitals and a kind of psychology

9

which brought some bitter days to Thomas Story Kirkbride (1), one of the stalwarts of American psychiatry and a man whose hospital provided a well-developed program of occupation, recreation, trips to the city for church or lectures, and patient participation in management of the institution with an atmosphere of optimism and mutual confidence all explicitly stated in the program—a truly therapeutic community.

The dreary battle went on through the rest of the nineteenth century and well into the twentieth although today the old wounds are healing more deeply with each passing year and less likely to be reopened by some fresh incident of loss of public confidence. On the other hand, the period was not without its constructive aspects. Many of the old records are gone and the intimate life of the institutions has become unclear with the passage of time but it is quite obvious that the mental hospitals of the last part of the century were far from completely closed institutions. There are to be found pictures of patient expeditions to nearby towns, parades, picnics and entertainments in the best modern tradition, and while the open hospital never had wide acceptance it was not for want of thinking of the idea. The debate was long and loud before it was passed over to remain buried and forgotten in the contemporary psychiatric literature until the question was reopened by recent developments. Craig Colony, a New York State hospital for epileptics operating since 1896, remained completely open until comparatively recent years and long maintained a policy of unsupervised patient visits to the neighboring town, and it still has a patients' organization, "The Colonists Club." From the start it practiced a type of industrial rehabilitation under the name of Sloyd and it has long had a grade of patient participation that would compare well with the most modern practices. Since the recent increased interest in liberalized treatment, we read of other institutions which had in whole or in part for long periods carried on the same tradition as, for example, the recent note on the fact that the Kalamazoo State Hospital has not used restraint for the last 50 years (5).

We see then that the name "therapeutic community" was unknown to previous periods, and many of the key technical procedures were undeveloped or rudimentary but the spirit and the idea are as old as the mental hospitals. This involves a liberal, humane, democratic, all embracing regime of hospital management for therapeutic purposes, the concept of a community of the mentally ill socially structured for therapeutic effect. It returned under various names, such as "moral treatment" and "non-restraint," or in the course of a crusade like that of Dorothea Linde Dix but never reached more than a part of the hospitalized mentally ill until the last few years when a world-wide trend of unprecedented scope has gotten under way.

The present movement is different in many ways from those which went before but still reflects their influence in general conception and even in many details of phraseology. However, the Therapeutic Community and its cousin, the Open Hospital, are concepts developed in their present form in England at the close of World War II.

THE BRITISH BORSTAL AND OTHER BRITISH INFLUENCES

It is interesting to speculate how much of this hospital change was a purely psychiatric development and how much reflects other trends and developments in Britain. One of the most interesting was the British Borstal system of correction for youthful offenders (6). This originated in an 1895 report which pointed out the prevalence of offenses among youths and the failure of existing methods as evidenced by the fact that the majority of habitual criminals were made between the ages of 16 and 21. Experimentation in segregation and special treatment was promptly begun and by the end of 1902 an entire prison at Borstal was devoted to this work. It is noteworthy that the Borstal system dealt to a material degree with problems of behavior similar to those treated later in the Therapeutic Community of Maxwell Jones. In 1923 a Borstal house plan copied after that of preparatory schools began to take shape and by 1930 open institutions were started. Among the important characteristics of the Borstal system were (1) team work of the staff, (2) emphasis on productive occupation, (3) preparation of the inmate for work in the community, (4) good relations with the surrounding district, and (5) review of matters pertaining to the prisoner with him.

Certain phrases describing the system have a familiar ring:

"Borstal training started as an experimental procedure. Its development has been the result of a continuous process of trial and error. . . . There is general realization that there is no one 'best way' to handle young offenders.

"The principle of flexibility holds good even in relation to selection of personnel: —the Commission seeks out a wide variety of the best possible personalities with different life experiences—and then turns them loose to grapple with the problem.

"Borstal institutions are communities in a sense unknown in most of reformatories. . . . a sense of living in a community which is by no means insulated from the activities and interests of normal life in town or country.

". . . a setting of socially interdependent relationships, and the deliberate direction of house or institution 'public opinion' . . . for its reformative value. The more nearly the microcosm of the institution can be made to resemble the outer world, especially the interrelationships—the more likely is the benefit to carry over into the larger society."

The Borstals were closed during World War II for lack of personnel but they represent a predecessor of much of the thinking with regard to the rehabilitation of the character disorders as later developed by Maxwell Jones and were created by the social climate in which the psychiatric developments took place.

During and after the war Britain experienced broad changes of social and scientific philosophy that have altered British life in a fundamental way. There was a turning to a synthetic as opposed to the analytic approach to a solution of problems; wartime pressures had forced the development of total organization and operational research and this appears to be reflected in the concept of the Therapeutic Community and in the Open Hospital.

The postwar social reform was marked by a great gain of the concepts of diffusion of authority, team work, and anti-authoritarianism in all branches of British life and a great emphasis on social problems. It would seem that these facilitated new adventures of

12

the pattern of the Open Hospital and Therapeutic Community in the mental hospitals of Britain.

THE FUTURE

However, this data does not provide us with a prognosis of the movement in America; it merely supplies a description and in some respects a diagnosis of the situation, especially in Britain, which made the undertakings possible and assured them of public support or at least tolerance when these long latent tendencies emerged again for trial and activation.

The question still remains, "What of the future of this country?" Will this movement suffer the fate of the humanitarian advances of the past? Must we apply the formulation of Earl Bond that only technical advances are secure and humanitarian ones may be swept away? If not, why not and how is the present situation different from those that went before? Can we rely wholly on the change in public attitude to hold these gains?

Great efforts have been expended in public education and their effects are palpable but the author believes that these alone would be an insecure protection. Several other factors appear to distinguish the present situation from all previous ones and these, together with the developing public attitude, give promise that the present favorable situation will not retrogress but is the start of a period of significant and progressive change:

a. The advances of the past were largely the work of a few dedicated and highly influential leaders. Today the movement is general and widespread, as if by common consent, and the entire profession is involved on a scale never before known.

b. Past advances were largely reactions against unfavorable conditions which usually had reached disgraceful and intolerable depths of deterioration before the public was prodded into action. The present one is by professional initiative and is built on the foundation of a gradually developed public confidence in the fundamental soundness of psychiatric practices. This, in turn, has been reinforced by the technical successes of the past 40 years. A therapeutic arma-

13

mentarium of malarial therapy and later the miracle of penicillin for paresis, the anti-convulsants, the long series of shock therapies and drug therapies have linked psychiatry to medicine and the treatment of mental illness to other treatment while the development of a rational psychodynamic therapy has actually put medicine into the debt of psychiatry; a growing consciousness of the psychopathology of everyday life has made it more and more difficult for the average man to dissociate himself from the mentally ill.

c. The virtual disappearance of disturbed behavior from the wards of mental hospitals generally, not merely from the favored few places where specially devoted and motivated staffs happen to exist for a time. Patients and visitors and staff alike no longer must make a special effort to compensate for their natural human reactions to a vivid display of hostile and aggressive emotions in others. The atmosphere of mental hospitals generally has attained a degree of relaxation not previously possible. The disturbed patient was always a threat to every liberal mental hospital program and at one time or another brought many, if not most, of them to an end, permanently or temporarily. This threat no longer hangs over us due to the availability of the newer methods of therapy.

d. Control of Overcrowding. For the first time in their history the mental hospitals of the United States and a number of foreign countries report a slackening of the need for hospital beds and in most instances a slow decrease. It appears now that the traditional overcrowding will, in the foreseeable future, become a thing of the past. There is no question that much of the turmoil and much of the behavior that led to security measures in the past were a direct expression of overcrowding. Simple lack of decent living space is itself a strong anti-therapeutic factor; its correction facilitates the creation of a therapeutic community.

e. Short-term mental hospital care is an accepted and established fact. For generations the general public and even the medical profession saw the mental hospitals as organizations for definitive care. Today it is widely understood that patients regularly leave mental hospitals to return to pro-

14

ductive lives. It is curious that this concept is best established with regard to those types of cases which have been traditionally cared for in mental hospitals but in the case of children and of the aged, two groups relatively new to mental hospital care, the tendency to demand definitive and long-term care is still strong.

The author is not inclined to think that we have solved all the problems which we face in the newly developing system of hospital care subsumed under the head of "the Therapeutic Community" and the "Open Hospital." Particularly the factor of cost must remain a stumbling block for the immediate future. We must also face the closely related problem of scarcity of properly trained personnel. In a sense, we must carry out a type of "bootstrap" procedure. Now that the mental hospitals are able to serve the psychiatric needs of their areas with a gradually decreasing number of beds it would seem that the decrease will be somewhat proportional to the adequacy of staffing and of financing while, on the other hand, the reduction in the chronic load of hospital cases frees funds and personnel for more intensive work with those that remain. It is to be hoped that for some time this process will show acceleration although one cannot be certain where a plateau effect will be found.

Now, in closing, we may hark back once more to Dr. Bond's comment. History bears out only too well his contention that advances of a purely humanitarian kind are quickly reversible while those based on technical advance are permanent. Since this seems to be so, the conclusion appears inescapable that we must try to base our advances on true scientific improvements as far as possible, yet at the same time we cannot slacken our efforts to maintain the humanitarian gains because much of the advance still remains in this area. It appears that part of the gains of psychiatry can be made self-perpetuating and in part they must be kept secure by unremitting effort.

BIBLIOGRAPHY

1. Bond, E. D.: *Dr. Kirkbride and His Mental Hospital.* Philadelphia, Lippincott, 1947.

2. Jones, M.: *The Therapeutic Community.* New York, Basic Books, Inc., 1953.

3. The Philosophers Library: *The Works of Plato.* Ed. Irwin Edam. New York, Simon and Schuster, 1928.

4. Kotinsky, R., and Witmer, H. C.: *Community Programs for Mental Health.* Cambridge, Harvard University Press, 1955.

5. Morter, R. A.: Non-restraint at Kalamazoo State Hospital. *Am. J. Psychiat., 115:* 557, 1958.

6. Healy, W., and Alper, B. S.: *Criminal Youth and the Borstal System.* New York, The Commonwealth Fund, 1941.

7. Deutsch, A.: *The Mentally Ill in America.* Garden City, Doubleday Doran, 1937.

DISCUSSION OF DR. BRILL'S PAPER

Dr. Alexander Gralnick:—

Is it possible that the present therapies we administer will be changed or discarded, as the therapeutic community becomes more prevalent? In other words, what effect will the therapeutic community have on the administration of physiological therapies? I would also ask this question: Why at this time are we returning to the concept of the therapeutic community?

I would like to address some remarks to Dr. Brill's paper. The historical perspective gives us reason to pause in humility. It would seem to me necessary to try to forestall the "relapse" which Dr. Brill points out has occurred so many times in the past. I will not pretend to have all of the answers, but would suggest that much will have to do with our own attitudes. I think psychiatrists tend to expect too much of themselves and consequently grasp for straws when something new comes up. Consequently, procedures which have been useful are too quickly discarded. Secondly, I would suggest, therefore, that we maintain a good degree of therapeutic optimism despite our relative ignorance. We should investigate the procedures we know much more thoroughly rather than be stampeded by every innovation. I think, too, we have to be strong enough to resist public and economic pressures for quick results. My plea is that we try to avoid what has happened to insulin therapy and other forms of treatment which have too quickly disappeared from the scene. If we are not careful, this may happen too with the work we are doing so enthusiastically with the therapeutic community.

Dr. ANTHONY HORDERN:—

I should like to observe that there are at least four significant differences between English and American mental hospitals. It seems to me important to be aware of these differences if one is to understand the different approaches that are followed in the two countries. Obviously, observations that are made under circumstances in Britain cannot apply exactly to American mental hospital patients who are hospitalized under different conditions.

In the first place, most British mental hospitals were built after the Industrial Revolution and, as such, were constructed some distance from the towns where they would be difficult of access, and where the mentally ill could be dismissed from the mind and their problem ignored. This isolation is still present in some degree, and since transportation—automobiles particularly—has not developed to the extent that it has in the United States, the patients in British hospitals find it difficult to gain immediate access to cities where they might cause disturbances. It is, therefore, much easier to open doors in the United Kingdom, where patients usually have large well-kept grounds in which to spend their time, in which they can be kept under adequate care, segregated from the community. In the second place, the vast bulk of mental hospital admissions in Britain today are voluntary patients, probably 70% to 80% at this time. It has been found that much greater cooperation can be obtained from both patient and relatives, if the patient can only be admitted without legal coercion and loss of civil rights. Of course, this sometimes has to be resorted to, but it is kept as a final recourse when no other possibility is available. I think you will all be aware that legislative steps are now being taken in Britain to attempt to diminish even the small amount of certification (commitment) that is presently taking place. In the third place, once patients are

17

admitted to good British mental hospitals, they are rapidly examined and, if necessary, placed on physical treatment without delay. Thus, an acute endogenous depressive might receive electroshock therapy on the day of his admission or the following day. Many have remarked this tendency of British medicine to be empirical; and the empirical tradition still flourishes in psychiatry particularly, where it seems to have borne therapeutic fruit. By contrast, the tendency one notices in some American hospitals today is a prolonged cautious waiting period prior to physical therapy during which the patient is assessed, and during which, if he be suicidal, his condition may very well give rise to anxiety in the hospital staff. The fourth and last point to which I wish to draw attention, is that in many of the better mental hospitals in Britain, patients are nursed in groups by interested attendants or nurses. All groups have regular work assignments. Some are trivial, merely sweeping up leaves, while alternatively some tasks are quite complicated, requiring a modicum of skill. Furthermore, and very important in my opinion, patients are paid for the work they do at a reasonable level of remuneration. It has even been possible in some hospitals to subcontract factory assembly work into the wards, where patients perform this type of work satisfactorily and contentedly with improvement in their behavior and self-respect. There was some initial difficulty with the trade unions over this problem, but it has been adjusted in progressive hospitals. It has always seemed to me very wrong indeed to expect patients who are shut up against their will anyway, to do a full day's work and receive no remuneration for it. This seems particularly relevant in the United States, where money, as Allport has shown, is a fundamental foundation of the way of life, a basis of cultural norm. One can do much more with patients if they are treated like normal human beings who are, we know, motivated in part by economic factors. I think the adverse effect of complete financial insufficiency and consequent total dependency on charity for such trivialities as cigarettes and clothing has been overlooked by many hospitals in this country, though Peffer's work in Perry Point Veterans Administration Hospital should be mentioned.

18

THE PLACE OF THE
THERAPEUTIC COMMUNITY
IN THE HISTORY AND DEVELOPMENT
OF A MODERN STATE HOSPITAL

R. A. Chittick, M. D.
G. W. Brooks, M. D.,
and
W. N. Deane, Ph.D.

INTRODUCTION

The therapeutic community is not merely a good hospital. It is a hospital in which concerted efforts are directed towards making each aspect of the patient's entire daily experience contribute to the ultimate goal of social and vocational rehabilitation. During the past four years, such a therapeutic community has gradually developed at Vermont State Hospital, in connection with efforts to achieve total rehabilitation of a large group of chronic schizophrenic patients. It is at present organized into a rehabilitation service housed in four centrally located open wards of 30 beds each. They are divided by a large central living room. Each ward houses two patient groups of 10 to 15 members each, who remain together in group therapy.

The hospital work with these patients has grown until it now includes eight major elements of treatment.*

The first and basic to all others is the very extensive use of drug treatment. About nine out of 10 receive some neuroleptic medication.

The second essential is the ward care program in which an effort has been made to secure an atmosphere as relaxed and non-custodial as possible within the traditional hospital structure. The attendants from these wards are included in discussion and planning groups. The wards are pleasantly decorated and furnished, have television, laundering facilities, etc. The patients have pets, make popcorn and plan parties. In short, we try to provide a more normal, homelike atmosphere.

The third element is the therapy groups started by Mr. Donald Eldred, our psychologist. Eight groups have been set up and used as group leaders—a sociologist, clinical psychologist, social worker, vocational counselor, physician, occupational therapist, nurse, and volunteer. They are conducted in many different ways by the variety of people involved. However, because they are

---

* Information on the three pages following was previously presented at the Osawatomie Institute on Chronic Schizophrenia and Hospital Treatment Programs held at Osawatomie, Kansas, October 1, 2, and 3, 1958.

21

included within the over-all atmosphere of a program directed towards social and vocational rehabilitation, the discussions tend to center around practical problems in job training, job finding, living arrangements, social activities, and the relevance of hospital activities to the patients' goals.

The fourth element is the system of graded privileges. Patients are able to progress rapidly from limited parole to freedom of movement within the entire hospital, and thence, to freedom of movement in the community. Many patients have cited this as a major element in their improvement. Doing their own personal shopping, going to the village for coffee and doughnuts, attending church, or just wandering about provides a very flexible testing ground for emerging self-confidence and social skills.

The fifth element is the introduction of graded group activities in the occupational therapy and recreation departments, designed to encourage or require group cooperation. They are arranged to direct the interests of the patients, first toward each other, then toward the entire hospital, and finally, toward the community. The patients prepare and serve meals for each other, help one another design and make clothing, put on a hospital bazaar, and make furniture and decorations for the newly opened rehabilitation houses. Last year, for the first time, they entered a float in the village Fourth of July parade and won first prize.

The sixth element is an expanded and intensified industrial therapy program which leads the patients from graded placements and trials in various hospital industries to daytime employment in the local community. This program is closely coordinated with the seventh feature, which is an intensified program of vocational counseling carried out by two full-time vocational counselors from the Vocational Rehabilitation Division. This leads through stages of vocational orientation, exploration, and finally, planning immediately preceding separation from the hospital.

The eighth element concerns other activities which further help to blur the boundaries between hospital and community.

22

A group of ex-patients calling themselves the "Helping Hands" return to visit the rehabilitation wards and hold discussion groups; week-end visits to the rehabilitation houses are provided for those having no homes or relatives to visit on week-ends; a series of parties for both in-hospital and ex-hospital rehabilitation patients are held alternately at the rehabilitation houses or within the recreation department at the hospital.

In order to coordinate all of these activities so that each contributes to the central goal for each patient, it has become necessary to develop many discussion and planning groups involving all staff members and patients in decision making. These have become so extensive that the key members' time in the therapeutic team is divided about evenly between contact with each other and with patients. There are twice-weekly planning conferences for all key members of the rehabilitation team, weekly group therapy meetings of about 12 patients each, a weekly discussion group with work supervisors and nursing supervisors, and a variety of other formalized policy and planning groups including the Vocational Rehabilitation Division, occupational therapy, recreation therapist, and others. However, perhaps equally important are a large number of informal, small group conferences held daily in the morning, at twice daily coffee breaks, etc. Such efforts at broadening the communication network have succeeded in sharing decision-making with attendants and patients.

RESULTS

Sixty-seven of the first 100 patients accepted into the program since July 1, 1957 have been released from the hospital. This represents 18 months' work. It is our expectation that with the passage of time there will be an even higher percentage of releases. Of those who left, 42 are employed full-time in the community, five full-time at the Vermont Sheltered Workshop, seven part-time, and 11 are in training programs. Two are unemployed; one living with his family in a dependent status, and the other is supported by government pension.

All this obviously represents a considerable departure from traditional state mental hospital practices. However, in trying to discover how these activities may have affected the hospital's experience in treating schizophrenic patients, we found that they seemed to merely continue progress that had been going on for some years.

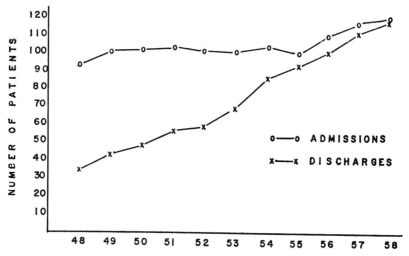

Fig. 1. — Admissions and discharges of schizophrenic and paranoid patients at Vermont State Hospital

Figure 1: This compares the total admissions of patients with schizophrenic and paranoid psychoses over the past 11 years with discharges over the same period. These are smoothed curves. The top line is the total admissions. The bottom line represents the annual discharges with these diagnoses. The patient is not considered discharged until he has successfully remained out of the hospital for at least six months. Our experience in discharging schizophrenics has steadily improved throughout the period. At the beginning, we discharged about 30 each year; at the end, 120. There is no marked change which could be attributed to the beginning of drug therapy in the hospital. The first point at which drug therapy might have affected the curve is in the discharges for the 1954-55 fiscal year, but the steady increase in discharges has merely continued.

24

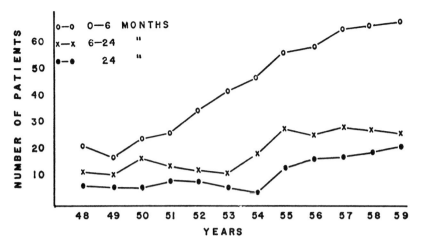

Fig. 2 — Discharges of paranoid and schizophrenic patients grouped by duration in months of hospitalization

Figure 2: The discharge figures are broken down according to duration of stay in the hospital, and the top line represents those discharged after less than six months in hospital. The curve resembles the over-all experience presented in Figure 1—a steady and rather rapid improvement. The midline represents those patients who have been in the hospital between six months and two years. There was little improvement in these discharge figures until 1953-54. The major improvement begins with the 1954-55 admissions and onset of drug therapy. The same is true of those chronic schizophrenics who had been hospitalized continually for more than two years. The bottom line is unchanged throughout the early part of the decade, averaging four or five each year, but has been steadily rising with drug treatment and the rehabilitation program.

DISCUSSION

Thus, it would seem that our therapeutic community has merely enhanced the hospital's improving results in the schizophrenias by extending these to the chronic group. We became interested in what changes in the hospital seemed to be correlated with this steadily improving discharge rate. The history of the hospital during this period shows most significant changes in nursing services and physical plant. During the decade, the number of attendants has increased from 109 to 278 with improvement in their status. The attendant-patient ratio has risen from 1:11 to 1:4. Attendants' salaries have increased from $.38 per hour to $1.12 per hour, and working hours declined from 60 to 40 hours weekly. Perhaps most important, very extensive and intensive attendant training and evaluation programs have been in effect for more than eight years. These changes have served to prepare attendants for increasing participation in the therapeutic program and to increase the administration's confidence in their abilities.

There has been a steady increase in the rated bed capacity from 800 to 1,200 with improvement in the general comfort of the hospital. Such has been made possible by a building program which included a medical-surgical unit and two ward buildings accommodating about 350 patients. Dormitories for attendants and nurses have also been constructed. Many wards have been redecorated and bars removed.

The hospital population has remained stable at about 1,200 patients for the last decade, thus permitting full advantage to be taken of the enlarged physical plant by preventing over-crowding. It seems to us that these developments point in the direction of a hospital experience which is totally therapeutic and away from the type of hospital which is designed merely to detain patients while more specific therapies are applied.

CONCLUSION

These findings demonstrate the existence of a trend toward the development of a therapeutic community in this hospital for some years before one was actually established. Indeed, it is difficult to see, if this had not been the case, how our results could have been obtained. Under different circumstances, the attempt to establish a rehabilitation service depending heavily on the sharing of planning and decisions with the attendants and patients would have been a movement against the existing trend, and this would have been reflected in much poorer results. It seems to us that these trends in our hospital parallel those in many other state hospitals in our culture. If this is true, the development should be capitalized upon wherever and whenever possible.

DISCUSSION OF DR. CHITTICK'S PAPER

Dr. Kenneth B. Moore:—

In discussing the problem of the therapeutic community, I believe it is necessary to make certain basic steps as a prerequisite for our efforts. We need to ask ourselves, what are our theoretical conceptions of human behavior and how can these be implemented in the design of the therapeutic community? What are our concepts of social, behavioral, and individual impairments which we see in the mentally ill patient and for which we attempt to set up conditions which will bring about change? If we can identify these, begin to measure them, and to relate them to the variables within the physical, social, and individual environments, we are in a better position to then manipulate social forces which may be related to such changes. It is very possible that once we have an adequate conceptualization of schizophrenia, and the specific social, neurological, perceptual, and even chemical impairments which are involved, our design of therapy may take somewhat different forms than we now anticipate.

For example, it may well be that the therapeutic climate for the schizophrenic may be something quite different from an attempt to recreate within the hospital a homelike environment, or one which reproduces what we now think of as desirable features of life outside a hospital. It may indeed be that such a therapeutic community may utilize, in a very specific way, social forces to reduce such things as disorganization or depersonalization through a meticulously controlled and rigid, rather than permissive attitude. While I don't believe this is the direction in which we will necessarily go, I do believe more studies designed to give us answers

27

to this question are needed. Certainly, we do know that a therapeutic environment for an adolescent will be much different than that for a geriatric patient.

Finally, I think we need to search for the characteristics which are common to different types of hospitals in order to gain further understanding of some of the general therapeutically social forces which are potentially possible within the mental hospital.

USE OF DRUGS TO MODIFY
THE SOCIAL BEHAVIOR OF ANIMALS

Samuel Irwin, Ph.D.

29

It is the purpose of this paper to show how drugs can and have been used to modify the social behavior of animals. It is by no means an exhaustive treatment, but it is hoped that its relevance and applicability to the modification of human social behavior will be apparent.

SOCIAL ORGANIZATION

Social organization is not unique to man. According to Collias (1), it is an all pervasive fact in the animal kingdom. Biological factors, such as an early period of immaturity and imprinting, lead to social interactions with the young which promote socialization and group formation. Both cultural and biological considerations influence the manner in which the group is organized. This largely is within a competitive-cooperative framework, with an evolutionary trend toward increased cooperation, increased complexity and increased control of the external environment by living organisms.

Dominance Hierarchies (Competition)

Intra- and interspecies dominance hierarchies based upon aggressive-submissive interactions are widespread among vertebrates (2). It is particularly well developed in flocks of chickens where each individual except the one at the bottom of the hierarchy may peck or threaten certain other individuals without being pecked in return (3, 4, 5). It is less well developed in animals lacking the sensory capacity to differentiate effectively between different members of their group, as in the mouse and rat (6).

Where individuals continue to live together, a social hierarchy based on habitual subordination promotes social harmony by stabilizing and formalizing the competitive relationships (7). In small groups or low population densities, strangers are more likely to be forcibly excluded or relegated to a low position in the hierarchy and the hierarchy more rigidly maintained (2, 8, 9). Shifts of dominance rank are more frequent in large groups, and the introduction of a large number of individuals to a small or

31

closely organized group may result in breakdown of the organization. In the stable, well organized hierarchy, the average individual is better provided for (7).

The despot in the dominance hierarchy has greater access to food, mates or territory (2, 10, 11). If he is abusive, *displaced aggression* is observed, i.e., the passing on of punishment from member to member down the hierarchy (2, 12). Removal of the dominant individual from the group, whether in cats (13), Rhesus monkeys (14), chickens (3), or children (15), results in a struggle for dominance by the immediate subordinates. Strongly dominated individuals tend to freeze into unresponsive immobility during exposure to novel situations, such as a maze or new environment (16).

Cooperative Behavior

The maintenance of cooperative relations in insects and vertebrates depends largely on the socialization of the young and accompanying inhibition of aggressive behavior (1). It has been carried to a further degree in the individual organism and intraspecies population than in the interspecies community, but it has evolved in all systems (17). It is the major framework of organization in such social insects as the ant, bee and termite and, among mammals, in sheep, howling monkeys, gerbils and chimpanzees (6). It is also observed in man, where cultural influences occasionally manage to inhibit his aggressive behavior for, among primates, humans rank near the top for aggressiveness (18).

In general, the social behavior of humans is more complex and more highly organized than in animals, but the basic components of group interaction are present and available for study in humans and animals alike, e.g., aggressive-submissive relationships, frustration, displaced aggression, identification, leadership, cooperative or contagious behavior, etc. Unfortunately, the most systematic experimental studies with drugs in animal populations has been with insecticides, rodenticides and odor repellants. This kind of study offers little insight to therapy, but a great deal on how to liquidate a community. Despite the importance of systematic, controlled studies of the effect of drugs on the social behavior of animal populations, much of the information available on the subject results from the empirical use of the drugs clinically.

OBJECTIVES OF DRUG THERAPY

The objectives of drug therapy in animals and humans are similar, namely, to promote social harmony, cooperative behavior and the social rehabilitation of the individual. A first step in the direction of social harmony is the control of aggressive-destructive behavior, now made possible by our more potent "tranquilizers." In general, when using depressants, group behavior can be modified pharmacologically either by treating the entire group or by medicating only the most disruptive or influential members of the group. Where the entire group is treated, depending on the dose employed, group behavior is influenced predominantly by the pharmacological properties of the drug. In the second instance, where only the most disruptive members of the group are treated, the effect on group behavior is a consequence of "removal" of the disruptive elements from the group. Group behavior then takes on the characteristics of the non-treated members. The latter situation can be considerably altered, however, if drugs are administered which increase activity and aggressiveness.

EFFECT OF DRUGS ON BEHAVIORAL PROCESSES

Locomotor Activity

The locomotor activity of a group is increased by psychomotor stimulants and decreased by psychomotor depressants. Treating only one member of a group may be sufficient to influence the activity level of the entire group, an effect greater with stimulants than with depressants. The change in group behavior results from the altered frequency of interactions brought about by the effect of treatment, and is a function of group size per unit area, dosage and the number of individuals treated.

By administering chlorpromazine to only one of six Rhesus monkeys, Varley and Delgado (19) noted a significant reduction both in the group activity and noise level. The effects increased as additional members of the group were treated. In studies with female Charles River rats placed in separate activity tread-wheels, but with treadwheels in close proximity, saline-treated animals exhibited abnormally higher activity counts if run concurrently with animals administered methamphetamine (Figure

INTERACTION EFFECT ON LOCOMOTOR ACTIVITY (RAT)

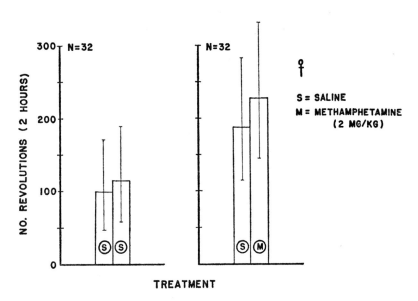

FIGURE 1—Interaction effect of stimulated animals on the locomotor be-havior of an unstimulated group. One hour after subcutaneous treatment, 16 saline-treated animals were placed alternately in 32 revolving tread-wheels adjacent to 16 control, saline-treated animals (left figure) or 16 methamphetamine-treated animals (right figure). In the right figure, the two-hour locomotor count of the saline-treated group was very much greater than the count of the control saline groups ($P = 0.1$) and did not differ significantly from the methamphetamine-stimulated group with which it was run.

1). The effect of group interaction also can influence the toxicity of a drug. For example, the lethality of amphetamine is increased over tenfold by the simple expedient of housing treated animals

34

together as a group rather than separately (20). Under similar conditions, group interactions tend to reduce the toxicity of psychomotor depressants.

Aggressive Behavior

The control of aggressive behavior is an important area of treatment. Threat of injury elicits apprehension, agitation, displaced aggression and an over-all breakdown of cooperative behavior patterns within the group. Often a single dose of drug can be curative. This is true where it is possible to establish, during the course of the drug action, more social behavior patterns which continue in the absence of drug. This is true in the treatment of animals that tend to cannibalize their newborn (21), in the treat-

AGGRESSIVE BEHAVIOR (RAT)

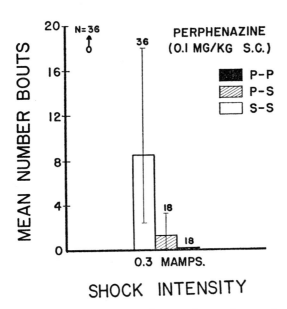

FIGURE 2—The number of fighting bouts of paired animals administered electroshock stimulation for three minutes was significantly reduced by "tranquilization" with perphenazine (Trilafon), even when only *one* of each pair of animals received the drug (S = saline; P = perphenazine).

ment of post-parturiant hysteria where animals attack man or beast, or under conditions of aggressiveness which, if repeatedly successful in outcome, tend to reinforce and maintain the behavior.

In Figure 2 is summarized the incidence of fighting when pairs of "tranquilized" and saline-treated animals are exposed to continuous electroshock stimulation for three minutes. The animals in this instance are highly socialized Charles River rats normally unaccustomed to fighting with one another. It will be noted that fighting bouts were almost reduced to zero when only one of the two animals was "tranquilized." An important factor, it seems, in whether or not an aggressive gesture culminates in a fight is the presence or absence of a *defensive response* by the non-aggressor. The absence of this response in the "tranquilized" animal aborted attacks by the saline-treated animal and markedly reduced the incidence of fighting. In the animal kingdom many animals learn to freeze into a passive position as a defense against attack, as with the oppossum and with animals of low position in a dominance hierarchy (16). It is also a device used by humans. Often it is dangerous to introduce a stranger into an aggressive community. Where the group size is small, the danger can be minimized by "tranquilizing" the entire group. In large communities, the transition is more conveniently accomplished by "tranquilizing" the stranger. The abolition of the aggressiveness or defensive behavior of the stranger minimizes the probability of its being injured by the group. An aggressive group also is more likely to accept a "passive" than aggressive stranger into its ranks.

Testosterone (6) and stimulant drugs such as iproniazid and methamphetamine promote aggressiveness by lowering the threshold of stimulation required to elicit fighting. The threshold-lowering effect of chronic iproniazid administration (5 mg/kg orally) is illustrated in Figure 3. It may be noted, however, that the incidence of fighting under supra-threshold conditions of electroshock stimulation did not differ significantly between the saline and iproniazid-treated animals. When animals are more intensely stimulated by drug, as with methamphetamine, significant differ-

AGGRESSIVE BEHAVIOR (RAT)

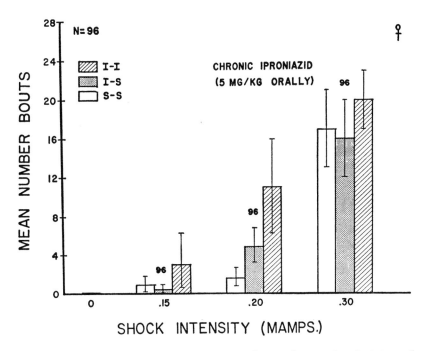

FIGURE 3—The number of fighting bouts of paired animals administered electroshock stimulation was significantly increased by the chronic administration of iproniazid, and also increased when only *one* of each pair of animals received the drug. Iproniazid had a threshold-lowering effect on aggressive behavior; the difference in aggressiveness between iproniazid (I) and saline (S) paired animals was not significant at higher (supra-threshold) shock intensities.

ences in fighting are produced even with supra-threshold stimulation.

Sexual Behavior

The threshold of stimulation required to elicit sexual behavior can be lowered by the administration of male or female sex hormones (6), and raised by relatively large doses of phenothiazine "tranquilizers." Where problems of aggressiveness or avoidance-inhibition prevent sexual relations, these problems can be over-

37

come and sexual behavior increased by relatively small doses of "tranquilizer." The drugs also have been used to facilitate artificial insemination.

Apprehension-Anxiety

A change in the environment or social group of an animal can evoke an intense stress response associated with apprehension, anxiety, agitation, increased locomotion and aggressiveness, depression, "shipping-fever" or even death (21, 22). Some animal strains are extremely sensitive to changes in their social environment. They may die within a month of being placed in a new social group. Certain strains of wild rats, held loosely and securely so that they cannot escape, become depressed and die within an hour. The syndrome leading to death is associated with cardiac and respiratory slowing; struggle behavior is not a factor. Problems of this kind arise during weaning, in the removal of cattle from native pastures, in their shipment to the stockyards, or placement in strange feed lots. Animals may refuse to eat or drink and lose considerable weight. All of this can be minimized or prevented by the administration of tranquilizing drugs such as perphenazine or chlorpromazine (21, 22, 23).

Imprinting

Imprinting is an extremely rapid form of learning that can take place only during a very brief, critical period. Although studied mainly in birds (24, 25), examples of imprinting have been reported in insects, fish and in some mammals, e.g., sheep, deer, buffalo, dogs and humans (26, 27, 28, 29, 30). For example, there is a critical period when dogs can be trained and when they can become accustomed to human beings. If dogs are not tamed during this interval they remain wild forever (6). A similar event takes place in humans. If a child is deprived of the mother or a mother-substitute during a critical period, the child develops apathy and/or asocial behavior (31). According to Huxley (32), imprinting in song birds does not take place until they are a year old or coming into maturity. He considers that this may have some bearing on the fact that human beings are subject to what he calls "a peculiar form of imprinting known as romantic love," which may take place when they reach puberty. The important point about imprinting is that there is a critical period in which it occurs, and that this period usually is quite brief.

Mallard ducklings show this effect only between twelve and seventeen hours after hatching (33). This can be expressed experimentally by the rapidity with which they learn to follow a moving object exposed to them during a brief period of time. According to Hess (34), the strength of the imprinting is directly related to the amount of muscular energy expended by the Mallard in getting to or following the object. It was not related to the amount of exposure time. Hess found that he could inhibit the imprinting of Mallards by the administration of meprobamate (25 mg/kg orally) during the critical age. As a consequence of this inhibition, the animals failed to exhibit the fear and avoidance behavior ordinarily observed after imprinting and during their adult life. The animals were no longer fearful of the approach of strangers, but also tended to remain apart from their own social group.

Resistance

Resistance is a phenomenon observed in both animals and man, and has been shown to increase during certain developmental phases of growth. In some instances it may be an outgrowth of imprinting or of a failure to imprint. A ewe, for example, will refuse to adopt a strange lamb but will do so if the lamb is covered by the skin of the ewe's deceased offspring. A problem also arises where animals refuse to suckle their own litter. The resistance in either case can be overcome by a single dose of chlorpromazine or perphenazine. The resistance of animals to handling, strangers, sexual submission, and to training also can be overcome by the use of "tranquilizing" drugs. Conversely, resistance is increased by psychomotor stimulants.

Contagious Behavior

Contagious behavior is prevalent in almost all animal species, including man. It is particularly evident in schools of fish which turn direction almost simultaneously following a stimulus. Contagious behavior is mimicking behavior, a tendency to follow the behavior of adjacent members of a group or of a group leader. Farmers use a trained "Judas" goat to lead their flock to market or to pasture and the same principle is used a facilitate the transfer of cattle or swine from cattle-cars to stockyard feeding lots Swine and certain strains of cattle are particularly irritable and unruly during such transfer. By tranquilizing the lead animals in a group, stockyard attendants are amazed at the ease of handling and processing of the entire group. In the contagious behavior of fish or ducks, where no specific group leader is present and where any individual in the group can provide the stimulus for a contagious response, it may be necessary to tranquilize a major portion of the group to reduce or abolish the contagious behavior.

CONCLUSION

In many respects the behavior of animals and humans are organized along similar lines and the objectives of therapy are essentially the same. In attempting to modify the behavior of a social group, it is not always necessary to medicate all its members. Treating the most disruptive individuals of the group may suffice to provide an atmosphere of social harmony conducive to the development of more social attitudes and behavior. As with humans, special problems are created when individuals are moved into a strange environment or social milieu. Drugs are useful in minimizing the stress that follows and in ameliorating the conflicts that arise. The response to a drug, however, is part of a complex *drug-personality-environment interaction.* Greater attention should be focused on the kind of environment, group composition and social organization most likely to promote a therapeutic response or social rehabilitation. The concept of a "therapeutic community" is a step in this direction and can find ample support in observations made with animals.

REFERENCES

1. Collias N. E.: Social Life and the Individual Among Vertebrate Animals. *Ann. New York Acad. Sci., 51:* 1074, 1950.

2. Collias, N. E.: Aggressive Behavior Among Vertebrate Animals. *Physiol. Zool., 17:* 83, 1944.

3. Schjelderup-Ebbe, T.: Beiträge zur Sozialpsychologie des Haushuhns. *Zeits. f. Psychol., 88:* 225, 1922.

4. Schjelderup-Ebbe, T.: Social Behavior of Birds. *Handbook of Social Psychology,* Edited by C. Murchison (XX): 947-973, 1935. Clark Univ. Press, Worcester, Mass.

5. Masure, R. and Alle, W. C.: The Social Order in Flocks of the Common Chicken and the Pigeon. *Auk, 51:* 306, 1934.

6. Scott, J. P.: *Animal Behavior.* Univ. of Chicago Press. Chicago, Ill., 1958.

7. Guhl, A. M. and Allee, W. C.: Some Measurable Effects of Social Organization in Flocks of Hens. *Physiol. Zool., 17:* 320, 1944.

8. Emlen, J. T., Jr.: Seasonal Movements of a Low-Density Valley Quail Population. *J. Wildlife Management, 3:* 118, 1939.

9. Howard, W. E. and Emlen, J. T. Jr.: Intercovey, Social Relationships in the Valley Quail. *Wilson Bull., 54:* 162, 1942.

10. Collias, N. E. and Taber, R. D.: Grouping and Dominance Relations Among Wild Ring-Necked Pheasants. *Anat. Record (Suppl.), 101:* 44, 1948.

11. Greenberg, B.: Some Relations Between Territory, Social Hierarchy, and Leadership in the Green Sunfish (Lepomis cyanellus). *Physiol. Zool., 20:* 267, 1947.

12. Katz, D.: *Animals and Men. Studies in Comparative Psychology.* Longmans, Green. New York, 1937.

13. Winslow, C. N.: Observation of Dominance-Subordination in Cats. *J. Genet. Psychol., 52:* 425, 1938.

14. Carpenter, C. R.: Sexual Behavior of Free Ranging Rhesus Monkeys (Macaca mulatta). II. Periodicity of Estrus, Homosexual, Autoerotic and Non-Conformist Behavior. *J. Comp. Psychol., 33:* 113, 1942.

15. Lewin, K., Lippitt, R. and White, R. K.: Patterns of Aggressive Behavior in Experimentally Created "Social Climates." *J. Soc. Psychol., 10:* 271, 1939.

16. Riess, B. F.: "Freezing" Behavior in Rats and its Social Causation. *J. Soc. Psychol., 24:* 249, 1946.

17. Emerson, A. E.: The Biological Basis of Social Cooperation. *Acad. Sciences Trans., 39:* 8, 1946.

18. Scott, J. P.: *Aggression.* Univ. of Chicago Press. Chicago, Ill., 1958.

19. Varley, M. and Delgado, J.: (Personal Communication, 1959.)

20. Chance, M. R. A.: Factors Influencing the Toxicity of Sympathomimetric Amines to Solitary Mice. *J. Pharmacol, 89:* 289, 1947.

21. Scheidy, S. F. and McNally, K. S.: Tranquilizing Drugs in Veterinary Practice. *Cornell Vet., 48:* 331, 1958.

22. Hibbs, C. M.: Use of Chlorpromazine in Swine. *Vet. Med., 53:* 571, 1958.

23. Walker, Donald F.: Clinical Observations of Trilafon in Large Animal Practice. *Abstracts of the First Symposia on the use of Tranquilizers in Veterinary Practice.* pg. 53, Schering Corp., Bloomfield, N. J., 1958.

24. Fabricius, E.: Zur Ethologie Junger Anatiden. *Acta Zool.,* fenn. *68:* 1, 1951.

25. Ramsay, A. O.: Familial Recognition in Domestic Birds. *Auk., 68:* 1, 1951.

26. Thorpe, W. H.: Some Problems of Animal Learning. *Proc. Linn. Soc. Lond., 156:* 70, 1944.

27. Baerends, G. P. and Baerends-van Roon, J. M.: An Introduction to the Ethology of Cichlid Fishes. *Behavior Suppl. 1:* 1, 1950.

28. Grabowski, U.: Prägung eines Jungschafs auf den Menschen. *Z. Tierpsychol., 4:* 326, 1941.

29. Darling, F. F.: *Wild Country.* Cambridge Univ. Press. London, Eng., 1938.

30. Hediger, H.: *Wild Animals in Captivity.* Butterworth. London, Eng., 1950.

31. Bowlby, J.: *Maternal Care and Mental Health.* World Health Organization, Geneva, Switz., 1952.

32. Huxley, J.: Discussion. *Ann. New York Acad. Sci., 67:* 732, 1957.

33. Ramsay, A. O. and Hess, E. H.: A Laboratory Approach to The Study of Imprinting. *Wilson Bull., 66:* 196, 1954.

34. Hess, E. H.: Effects of Meprobamate on Imprinting in Waterfowl. *Ann. New York Acad. Sci., 67:* 724, 1957.

DISCUSSION OF DR. IRWIN'S PAPER.

DR. DON R. LIPSITT:—

Although the phenomenon of imprinting may have applicability to the learning processes of animals, it smacks too much of the ancient "tabula rasa" theory of learning to be very acceptably applied to humans. Nonetheless, the animal studies referred to by Dr. Irwin emphasize the importance of timing in learning behavior. Scott[1] has described a critical period in dogs during which taming can be accomplished most readily. Stendler[2] has suggested two such critical periods in the socialization of the child and has further emphasized that what happens to the child during those times strongly influences the transition from dependency to independence and subsequent psychopathology. Rogg[3], in recounting his experiences with several schizophrenic patients, has suggested that at some point in the patient's illness, there exists an "opportunity" for the patient to either accept or reject his illness, and that the way in which this pivotal "time of decision" is handled by both patient and therapist will determine his choice. What seems to be implied by all these authors is that ability to learn is intimately related to significant interactions, whether between dog and tamer, child and parent, or patient and therapist, and that the timing of certain learning experiences or traumatic events relative to this dependent relationship will have a profound effect upon personality and behavioral development. Restated in this way, imprinting is a learning phenomenon of which psychoanalysis has long been aware.

This timing factor would seem to be of special significance in the therapeutic approach to the large number of chronic patients in mental hospitals. If there are indeed such critical periods of growth and development in the process of socialization, then it would seem relevant to ask whether such times occur only once and are irreversible, or whether the regressed, desocialized indi-

1 Scott, J. P.: Critical period hypothesis. *Personality*, 1: 162, 1951.
2 Stendler, C. B.: Critical periods in socialization and overdependency. *Child Development*, 23: 1, 1952.
3 Rogg, S. G.: Time of decision. *Psychiat. Quart.*, 24: 243, 1950.

vidual again goes through similar critical periods as his treatment proceeds toward ultimate resocialization and rehabilitation. If such is the case, then the sense of timelessness which seems to pervade many chronic institutions could more appropriately be replaced by a sensitivity to critical periods in the hospital when the judicious use of drugs and the timely introduction of therapeutic measures might well facilitate and expedite a sort of reimprinting which will help the patient make the difficult transition from chronicity and institutional dependency to resocialization and maximal self-sufficiency.

PRINCIPLES OF RESEARCH
IN A THERAPEUTIC COMMUNITY

A. F. Meszaros, M. D.

INTRODUCTION

This paper deals with the problems arising out of research in a psychiatric hospital during the development of a therapeutic community. These are not results of a systematic study but rather impressions and thoughts gained during the structuring of such a milieu, and by an analysis of the literature (1-8).

Research might appear as a peripheral problem in the complex issue of therapeutic community. However, I intend to show that research is inherent in its structure and function. I also will demonstrate that, by incorporating research in a therapeutic community, new objectives and new research work methods can be brought into focus.

Like treatment and many other facets of psychiatric work, research is influenced by the milieu in which it is carried out. The object and the preferred method of research is usually shaped by the ideas and concepts which bind the milieu into a definable unit. Conversely, research may shape or modify the milieu in which it is initiated, may direct attention to problems which heretofore have not been recognized.

DEFINITION OF THE THERAPEUTIC COMMUNITY

It is generally recognized that mental illness is maintained not only by the patient's internal dynamisms but also by the interaction between the patient and his environment. The illness is maintained and often aggravated by the response of the social environment to the patient and to his mode of living. Then, treatment of the mentally ill patient should include the treatment of his social milieu. The establishment of the therapeutic community was, I believe, motivated by a belief in the effectiveness of social therapy—a therapy designed for the manipulation of emotional forces, attitudes and expectations which surround the patient. The therapeutic community provides a corrective social climate in which the patient can re-live and purge irrational fears surrounding previous relationships and can attempt more constructive and healthier social relationships.

Treatment of the patient and his milieu requires study of the socio-pathology of the immediate environment as well as study of the individual's psychodynamics. Treatment milieus differ according to the patterns of interaction between the people in the milieu, by the degree of freedom, protection and information available to the members in the group, and by the goals towards which the activity of the group is orientated. A milieu, such as the orthodox authoritarian one, may be oriented towards control; another, like the ideal therapeutic community, may be directed towards finding the optimal balance between freedom, protection and self-expression. A therapeutic community could be further characterized by the presence of self-regulatory social mechanisms operating in the treatment unit. In this way, control is introduced, not in the form of one authority figure, but in the group's desire to achieve a goal with a minimum of frustration.

RESEARCH IN A THERAPEUTIC COMMUNITY

The concept of self-regulation implies that the observation and recording of interactions are essential aspects of the life of the therapeutic community. Consequently, research cannot remain something exogenous but must become an organic part of the life of the community. The concept of self-regulation also implies a shift in emphasis, from the study of unrelated individual patients, to the qualitative study of interpersonal mechanisms and object relationships. Therefore, definition of the position and the role of the research worker, his focus of attention and his methods of collecting data, are necessary.

The basic objective of research in a therapeutic community is the observation of the patient in relation to his milieu. The people in the milieu, that is, the other patients and the personnel, are included in the study and are assessed as to their relationship to each and to the patient. The traditional patient-centered and symptom-oriented observation is replaced by a multi-personal approach (9) and by the study of the behavior and attitude of several individuals in regards to a specific situation. The situation is defined by delineating the life space of the community and of the individual members. Research work begins with the description of the socio-affective characteristics of the patient and of the milieu. The role of the patient as seen and enforced by the personnel, becomes an important item in the description. The reputation of the patient is regarded as a characteristic of both the patient and his social milieu. The reputation can be gauged by the interpersonal patterns of isolation, rejection or ambivalence. The characteristics of the average patient, of the most isolated patient, or of the most rejected individual in the community, are used as focal points in the description of the treatment milieu.

Attitudes and expectations of the personnel are described in relation to the principal functions of personnel, such as control, support and assistance. Relationships are described in terms of closeness-distance, dominance-submission, trust-fear, and degrees of identification between the members of the community. The disciplinary functions of control, the setting of standards and the means of enforcing standard behavior, are contrasted with the responses of the patient, such as compliance, automatic obedience or rebellious and disruptive behavior. The functions of support and assistance are viewed in relation to the idiosyncrasies of the personnel and of the patients, in relation to the existing patterns of antagonism, hostility, exploitation and in relation to the patterns of closeness, intimacy and identification. The role of the personnel as objects of identification receives particular consideration. The patient's acceptance of the personnel as models of identification and also the personnels' acceptance of these roles are studied.

Data regarding the above areas may be obtained by the research worker's direct observation, through questionnaires, or through the medium of spontaneous reports from the personnel. Among these methods, the spontaneous narrative and ventilation in the group conference, recorded and evaluated by the research worker, is the source of information in best accord with the principles of a therapeutic community. The research worker has an active role in the reporting and the evaluation of conferences on the ward. His observations are useful when dealing with subjectivity which may color assessment, and his contributions may help the

49

group towards achievement of a consensus of viewpoints and opinions.

The evaluation of the data requires a frame of reference which takes into account the characteristics of the psychiatric milieu. Unlike any other social situation, the psychiatric milieu is characterized by the heavy influence of unconscious and symbolic processes on social perceptions and on the reaction and counter-reaction patterns. For example, the interaction of schizophrenic patients with each other and with ward staff cannot be adequately studied without reference to the peculiarities of the patients' object relationships and without reference to the threats, anxieties and counter-reactions which the daily prolonged exposure to unconscious material evokes in the personnel.

Communication with hospitalized patients often creates acute anxiety and the personnel is often threatened with the break-through of their own unconscious conflicts. Maintaining distance and authority often serves as a protection for the personnel, but the distancing also increases tension and mutual anxiety. Many patients, because of their distorted social perceptions and because of the inadequate barrier between the inner and outside world, are deeply affected by staff attitudes. Defensive responses to anxiety, by both patients and staff, may set in motion a circular reaction leading to disruption of the treatment unit. These anxieties often lead to autism and other disruptive patterns among the patients, and to excessive control, to punishment or to expulsion of the patient by the personnel. Because of the nature and intensity of the emotional reaction within the psychiatric milieu —person to unconscious, person to person—it is necessary to apply dynamics of interpersonal events as well as status-role concepts. The concepts of psychoanalytic theory, particularly those which immediately refer to the dynamics of present interpersonal events, may complement the understanding of the traditional person to person interaction. Hence, a perfect union of sociology and psychoanalysis can do much to develop the understanding of any therapeutic community.

50

SOMATIC TREATMENTS IN A THERAPEUTIC COMMUNITY

The research worker who participates in a therapeutic community is in the position to diagnose and to interpret the self-perpetuating disruptive interaction patterns in the treatment milieu and may also suggest treatment measures. Treatment of individual patients within a therapeutic community may have effects on the whole treatment milieu (10). Changes in the patterns of relationships, in the activity level of the whole ward, in the extent and form of communications, and in the policies governing discipline and self-expression, may result from the treatment which was originally designed for individual patients. In treating each patient, a question as to the meaning of the specific treatment measure in regards to interactions within the group may be raised. Similarly it is pertinent whether the treatment measure promotes the group towards the ideal of the therapeutic community. The benefits which may be obtained from somnolent doses of sedatives and tranquilizers, from isolation or ECT, must be measured against the threat of exclusion and fear of punishment which such type of treatment invokes in the group. On the other hand, I have found in a previous work (11) with chronic schizophrenic patients, that pharmacological treatment may have beneficial effects, not only directly on the treated patients but also on the non-treated patients. The improvement of the non-treated patients results from changes in the interaction patterns within the treatment milieu. As a result of treatment, the hostility and fear of closeness which were manifest in the behavior and attitudes of patients and the personnel, are replaced by more accepting and tolerant attitudes on both sides.

According to the principles of a therapeutic community, the main object of study is the interpersonal meaning of the behavior, attitudes and thought content of the patient. The symptoms are regarded as expressions of the needs and expectations of the patient and as responses to the social environment. Consequently, the research worker seeks to explore the effects of pharmacological treatment on the relationships of the patient with his immediate social environment. In this connection, I would like to call attention to the difficulties which we have encountered with the

51

anti-depressant drugs. The treatment responses have been varied and, in many instances, there has been a conspicuous time interval before changes have occurred. During the early phase of treatment there is sometimes a period of aggressive over-activity and a free indiscriminate expression of feelings and attitudes on the part of both staff and patients. Delay in treatment response may depend on the tolerance, skill and stability of the personnel who are faced with the conflict of dependency and aggression emanating from the patient. The emergence of defensive hostility, the need for control of these hostilities, and also the need for meeting the patient's demands for protection and dependency, prove to be very taxing to the personnel. The overt and concealed conflicts aroused in the personnel by this behavior may lead to prolongation and aggravation of the patient's illness. It may call for immediate relief measures.

Regarding another fairly recent drug, trifluperazine, several observers have reported good results with withdrawn, inactive patients. I have the impression that its effectiveness depends on the patient-personnel relationship. Good results have been obtained in those instances where inactivity is associated with a mutual rejection between patients and personnel. Poorer results have been obtained where inactivity is associated with a milieu of apathy and isolation. Whereas in the former instance, the results have been rather encouraging and have led to communication and rapprochement following the administration of the drug, in the latter situation, the treatment results have not been so evident.

The foregoing would indicate that the method of multi-personnel situation-analysis is eminently suitable for research in a therapeutic community. However, the situation-analysis is essentially an observational approach and creates great difficulties for the investigator if he wants to adhere to objective investigative techniques and statistical validation. For situation-analysis, the number of descriptive and dynamic variables by which the patient and his situation can be identified, is most essential. Numerous descriptive and dynamic variables could offer greater validity and greater richness than could one or two variables such as diagnosis or leading clinical symptom. Statistical studies are valuable when isolated symptoms are investigated; however, when reciprocal patterns of interactions, attitudes and expectations are selected as targets for treatment and research, then open observational methods are more suitable.

The technical devices of selecting control patients (12, 13), use of placebo and double-blind studies (14) have been designed mainly for the control or elimination of the interpersonal factors in the research design. However, differences in interpersonal relations may remain, in spite of careful selection of the group according to clinical and biological criteria, and may significantly influence the results of treatment (15). The alternative to a rigid experimental design would be the application of situation-analysis to pharmacological research. By this approach, drug effects may be examined together with a socio-psychiatric study of the treatment milieu. This method makes it possible to investigate those interpersonal relationships which facilitate or inhibit the effect of physical and pharmacological treatment.

THE RESEARCH WORKER IN A THERAPEUTIC COMMUNITY

The therapeutic community is likely to change the position of the research worker. His status as an independent observer is likely to suffer and he will enter into the life of the community which he investigates. He is in close daily contact with patients and staff. He is available for observation and interpretation of the dynamics of the community. The group reacts to his personality and his function will modify the life of the community. He participates in group discussions and also in various spontaneous incidents on the ward. He shares his functions, observations and reporting with other members of the group. In a therapeutic community, the function of observation is not divorced from interaction but becomes subordinated to it. The "independent observer" is likely to be replaced by group discussions. Formal notes and rating scales give way to spontaneous comments and to non-technical informal diaries. There is ample room, within the frame of research, for spontaneity and subjectivity on the part of the observers.

Contrary to practices in other branches of psychiatric research, findings in these studies are intended primarily for the information of the therapeutic community. This feed-back function of research is an important aspect of the therapeutic community. The outlined research policy is in accord with, and is necessitated by, the principles of a therapeutic community, but it deviates in some respects from the customary requirements of validity and from a rigidly controlled objective research design. However, the reliability and communicability of the findings can be safeguarded by the orientation of the personnel to the principles of the therapeutic community. Therefore, an intensive teaching program is necessary for the refinement of observations, would foster the development of consistent viewpoints, and make continued situation-analysis possible.

CONCLUSION

Research, in order to be useful to the therapeutic community, has to adapt its methods and objectives to the treatment milieu which is under investigation. There is a need for clear, concrete definition of the goals of the given community. The research worker has the task of discerning the ways and means by which a treatment policy is implemented and of evaluating the effect of treatment on the patients and personnel. The meaning of the term "treatment" is extended to include the interpersonal influences which the patient experiences throughout the hospital day. The interpersonal influences and interaction patterns are alterable through staff training and through the direct treatment procedures. The effects of teaching and treatment are reflected in the changing patterns of interactions in the treatment milieu.

The staff-patient interactions are examined on the level of hierarchy and status and on the level of primitive, unconscious dynamisms. Therefore, the needs and vulnerabilities of the patients are compared with complementary counter-reactions in the personnel. In the analysis of the treatment situation, the concepts and hypotheses which are available from work with individual patients, are applied in the day-to-day observation of the people who share the same community.

BIBLIOGRAPHY

1. Sullivan, H. S.: Socio-psychiatric research. Its implications for the schizophrenia problem and for mental hygiene. *Am. J. Psychiat., 10:* 977, 1931.

2. Rowland, H.: Interaction processes in the state mental hospital. *Psychiatry, 1:* 323, 1938.

3. Hyde, R. W., and York, R. H.: Technique for investigating interpersonal relationships in a mental hospital. *J. Abn. Soc. Psychol., 44:* 287, 1948.

4. Devereux, G.: The social structure of a schizophrenia ward and its therapeutic fitness. *J. Clin. Psychopath. and Psychother., 6:* 231, 1944.

5. Stanton, A. H., and Schwartz, M. S.: The mental hospital. New York, Basic Books Inc., 1954.

6. Caudill, W., Redlich, F. C., Gilmore, H. R., and Brody, E. B.: Social structure and interaction processes on a psychiatric ward. *Am. J. Orthopsychiat., 22:* 314, 1952.

7. Cameron, J. D., Laing, R. D., and McGhie, A.: Effects of environmental changes in the care of chronic schizophrenics. *The Lancet, 2:* 1384, (Dec. 31) 1955.

8. Greenblatt, M., Levinson, D. G., and Williams, R. H.: The patient and the mental hospital. Illinois, The Free Press, 1957.

9. Racamier, P. C.: Introduction à une sociopathologie des schizophrènes hospitalisés. *L'Evolution Psychiatrique, 1:* 47, 1957:

10. Pollack, B.: Drug therapy—Clinical and operational effects. *Mental Hospitals, 7:* 14, 1956.

11. Meszaros, A. F., and Gallagher D. L.: Measuring indirect effects of treatment on chronic wards. *Dis. Nerv. Syst., 19:* 167, 1958.

12. Kline, N. S.: Samples and controls in psychiatric research. *Psychiat. Quart., 27:* 474, 1953.

13. Leveton, A. F.: The evaluation and testing of psychopharmaceutic drugs. *Am. J. Psychiat., 115:* 232, 1958.

14. Tuteur, W.: The "double-blind" method: Its pitfalls and fallacies. *Am. J. Psychiat., 114:* 921, 1958.

15. Sabshin, M., and Ramot, J.: Pharmacotherapeutic evaluation and the psychiatric setting. *A.M.A. Arch. Neurol. Psychiat., 75:* 362, 1956.

A THERAPEUTIC COMMUNITY: ANALYSIS OF ITS OPERATION AFTER TWO YEARS

Herman C. B. Denber, M. D.

Therapeutic community as applied to the research division ward at Manhattan State Hospital is considered an operation where emphasis is placed on inter- and intra-group relations between patients, nurses and physicians; where mental illness is understood as a deviant form of behavior to be treated in the same frame of reference as physical illness with all chemical, physiological and psychological techniques available; and where the ward operates as closely as possible to the actual everyday community life.

The first therapeutic community probably began in Geel, Belgium, as early as 1236 when insane patients were cared for by private families. This process has been extended over 720 years later to some 2,000 patients who live and work in families in the city and are seen periodically by psychiatrists and nurses of the "Rigscolonie de Geel" (1).

Walk (2) has reviewed extensively the "moral treatment of the insane," indicating that present interest is merely a revival of what has existed off and on for over 100 years. Jones (3) recently analyzed his operation of a therapeutic community over a long period of time with social deviants. Wilmer (4) demonstrated that the psychiatric receiving ward in a naval station could be managed along these principles. Greenblatt, *et al.* (5), as well as Hargrove and Schlosser (6) have underscored succinctly the many problems inherent in state hospitals which must be overcome before a therapeutic community can be activated. The sociological determinants of group interaction which subserve this operation have received close attention (7-8).

The extremely important problem of remunerative work in psychiatric hospitals has received little notice in this country, but has been studied at length in a series of articles in the Lancet (9) and by a special bulletin of the French Ministry of Health (10), as well as in a preliminary report from this hospital (11).

Although an intensive chemotherapy program was under way in this ward for two years, many aspects of modern psychiatric therapies were lacking. A plateau effect was observed in which improvements were stabilized without additional progress. Much has been written about the social factors operant in psychoses, and they are even held to be primary (12). If alterations in the ward social structure would produce significant changes in behavior, more rapid discharge of recently admitted patients, improvement of chronic patients and facilitation of the general ward operation, some substance might then be attached to these hypotheses. For such reasons a therapeutic community was activated.

The ward houses between 70-86 legally committed, unselected acute and chronically ill female patients of various races and low socio-economic status in a state hospital with 3,000 patients adjacent to the borough of Manhattan in New York City. The staff at this writing is composed of two physicians, one nurse, three practical nurses and eight attendants on all shifts. The general physical structure and facilities are adequate. The doors of the ward are open all day. The therapeutic frame of reference represents a fusion of drug, physiological, and psychoanalytic treatments, with chemotherapy being the most important followed by group and individual psychotherapy.

Physicians, nurses and patients meet every Wednesday in the dayroom with the author as group leader. This is followed by a formal staff conference, although such meetings are held informally throughout the week. The patients meet as a group without any staff in attendance on Thursday morning, electing their own chairman and secretary. Patients are seen by the psychiatrists at any time during the week upon request. Evaluation of this operation is being made directly by members of the staff.

THE WARD BEFORE APRIL 1957

One ward in a two-story, four-ward 61-year-old continuous treatment building was assigned by the hospital administration to the research division in April 1957. This was a random selection without any specific reason. The patient population was composed of chronic cases with those who had relapsed on convalescent care and returned to the hospital. Their ages ranged from 19 to 70 years (Table 1). Sixty-five were schizophrenics (Table 2),

TABLE 1
AGES

Up to 19 1
20 - 29 13
30 - 39 27
40 - 49 23
50 - 59 13
60 - 69 3
70 and over 1

TABLE 2
DIAGNOSTIC CATEGORIES

Schizophrenia
    Paranoid 30
    Catatonic 14
    Other Types 13
    Hebephrenic 5
    Simple 3

Involutional
    Melancholia 3
    Paranoid 3
    Mixed 1

Manic-Depressive
    Manic 3
    Depressive 1

Psy. due to Alcohol 1

Psychoneurosis
    Reactive Depression 1

Psy. with Epi. Enceph. 1

Psy. with Men. Def. 1

Primary Behavior Disorder,
Simple Adult Maladjustment 1

TABLE 3
DURATION OF HOSPITALIZATION

Up to 1 year 16
1-2 years 18
2-3 years 16
3-4 years 3
4-5 years 8
5-10 years 12
10-20 years 5
Over 20 years 3

and the duration of continuous hospitalization varied from one month to 30½ years (Table 3). Many had repeated admissions and all forms of treatment had been tried. Daily rounds were made by the single ward physician. There were no formal meetings or communication between medical and nursing staff nor between staff and patients. No structured daily occupational program existed, although some patients attended the occupational therapy workshop, while others worked in various hospital industries. The doors were locked and all windows barred. No patients were allowed on the grounds unescorted by staff, except those with honor cards.

THE WARD AFTER APRIL 1957

The first changes made consisted in rearranging the stereotyped furniture. Almost all of the benches were removed from corridors and dayroom. Through appropriate positioning of furniture, the latter was divided into four separate areas. The television set was removed from its 12 foot high shelf and placed at eye level in one corner of the room. The walls were decorated with pictures and curtains were hung. Plants were placed on different tables and a fish tank secured. Patients were no longer permitted to congregate in their rooms or on the ward. They were directed to some occupation on the ward or elsewhere in the institution.

The two ward psychiatrists and nursing staff met at frequent intervals to discuss the new operation. Patients and personnel began to meet together on a weekly basis. The former were encouraged to participate in various ward activities and a system of work for pay was initiated. Fifteen jobs were allocated and patients performing any of these received five dollars per month. Nurses were asked to delegate many of their tasks to patients, i.e., opening the ward door, ground walks, etc. A sewing room and beauty parlor were opened on the ward and regular state issue clothing gradually replaced by attractive dresses. Patients were seen daily and were told repeatedly that no punitive action would be taken in spite of critical remarks addressed to the personnel or their policies. To this end, a suggestion box was placed on the ward. Regular monthly birthday parties were inaugurated. A day-long outing was held during July and August 1957 in a park 40 miles from the hospital. Whenever possible, patients were taken out for walks, play or into the city for personal shopping or sightseeing.

Much attention was given to personal hygiene and dress. The shower room was made available all day long; patients were requested to wear their own clothes, and articles of a personal nature were provided where lacking.

In the regular Wednesday morning meetings, patients were asked for their feelings and thoughts on all subjects pertaining to the ward operation. Their ideas were solicited with regard to improvements. Since this was their temporary "home," suggestions were invited to improve the conditions. The dietitian was asked in to discuss regular complaints regarding food. The group decided what corrective measures were to be taken where patients continuously violated ward rules. Occasionally interpretative remarks were made concerning a patient's behavior in the group, and at times some patients made realistic critical comments concerning others in the ward.

In the meetings with nurses, attention was focused on the group dynamics; on their new role as related to a previously classical custodial indoctrination; and on the shift in focus from "watching" to "awareness." Methods were explored for increasing their participation in the therapeutic process and for creating new tech-

63

niques of occupational therapy adaptable to the ward. Much effort was given to make them more aware of themselves as active members of the therapeutic team and of the influence exerted by both positive and negative unconscious processes on the daily ward operation. It was brought out that personal fears ("the supervisor will give it to me") often had a decisive effect on their attitudes towards further liberalization of the ward rules. The possibility of "an open ward" was discussed frequently and their own reactions solicited.

A closer relationship was established with non-medical personnel in the hospital, i.e., the business officer. Requests for changes, new equipment, additional food for parties were always accompanied by a detailed explanation of their importance and meaning in relationship to this new operation.

RESULTS – GENERAL

The drab monotony and uniformity inherent in the previous ward physical structure was changed into one of diversity. The entire ward was repainted and walls redecorated by the patients while their rooms assumed a certain individuality with personally made curtains, spreads and floor mats. Flowers and additional plants were placed throughout. Clothes became personable and sneakers were no longer worn. Even the most chronically ill patients visited the beauty parlor. The older chronic group benefited through the younger patients' interest as their sense of intragroup spirit developed. Pressing irons, scissors, pins, needles, and other instruments were made available in the shops for patients' use as various restrictive rules were abrogated.

All female patients who relapse on convalescent care are returned to this ward. When such readmissions took place at infrequent intervals (1-2 per week), the ward social structure absorbed them without incident. Occasionally up to 10 new patients were readmitted within one week, and on these occasions many other patients reacted with a recrudescence of symptoms. The ward became noisy; patients refused medication, and some stated openly that they were "afraid of these women." One Wednesday the patients voted to request transfer of agitated patients to another ward. One of the latter suddenly arose and made an incoherent plea, the essence of which was "don't throw me out of this ward because I'm so sick." The patient who had led the move for transfer arose and apologized for such an inhuman gesture on her part. This was roundly applauded, and since that time all patients entering the ward are received on an equal basis.

There was an initial burst of activity during the first six months in all directions which later began to diminish and find a plateau. Staff participation was absolutely and constantly necessary, as well as continuous urging of the more chronic patients. One group planted flowers and vegetables in the garden. The lack of a reasonable and rapid yield led to discouragement and eventual abandonment of this project. The ward newspaper functioned effectively as long as patients capable of writing material were present. The beauty parlor was in operation only while skilled patients were in the ward. Afterwards it was opened occasionally. Lack of trained personnel seriously hampered many projects aimed at occupying the patients throughout the day with industry type work.

In May 1957, the first door of the ward leading out to the back garden was unlocked during daylight hours. This led to greater freedom of movement in and out of the ward with no particular untoward results. It was observed frequently at the outset, and occasionally afterwards, that nursing staff would "forget" and "accidentally" close the door.

The ward atmosphere perceived the moment one entered has changed completely. The stultifying silence that often alternated with shrieking outbursts has been replaced by purposeful activities. Actually fewer than 10 patients can be seen on the ward during the day, and these represent the chronic deteriorated schizophrenic group. Since personal articles are no longer removed from patients upon admission, there is more of a sense of individuality than mass conformism. Restraint and seclusion have been abolished; although during the entire time of this report only one patient spent three hours in a seclusion room.

The bars on the dayroom windows were removed in June 1957 giving this area at least the appearance of a general hospital.

65

It was felt by November 1957 that indoctrination of staff and patients had arrived at a point where the ward doors could be opened; the first in the hospital with both acutely ill recently admitted as well as chronic patients. The ward is open all day until 4:30 p.m. in the winter, and 6:30 p.m. in the summer months. Patients may, however, take walks in groups after these hours.

The policy of city visits was liberalized so that patients in groups of two to five went to museums, motion pictures, or places of public interest. Weekend home visits have been extended at times to four days.

In view of the frequent delay in social service investigations, a project was begun where patients went to the city for jobs and then lived in the hospital and worked out. This has materially accelerated separation from the hospital in some cases (13).

After securing authorization in April 1958 from the various governmental agencies, a workshop was opened on the ward. Here, patients worked on contracts secured from manufacturers in the city, and were paid on a piece work basis with a minimum wage set by the United States Department of Labor. This has functioned well, and some chronically ill patients have been effectively employed in this shop (11).

There appeared to be little difference in the number of patients placed on convalescent care or discharged in the 1956-58 period

TABLE 4
PLACEMENT ON CONVALESCENT CARE AND DISCHARGE

Year	Number of Patients
1953	21
1954	37
1955*	101
1956	56
1957**	87
1958	73

*Large scale chemotherapy introduced.
**Ward operation as therapeutic community began in April 1957.

(Table 4). The fluctuations during these years more probably depended upon the physicians in service at these times. The sharp upswing in 1955 corresponded to the introduction of the new drugs, leaving thereafter a residue of the more chronic cases. The latter probably explains the low figure in 1956. The upswing in 1957-58 represents, it would seem, the intensive treatment program reported herein. In 1958 we were able to send the first long-term patient into the community after a 19-year hospitalization.

There were two unsuccessful suicidal attempts during this time and one episode of destructiveness.

THE GROUP MEETINGS

Initially it was difficult to assemble all of the patients on Wednesday morning; some flatly refused to participate, while others were too disturbed. Seats were arranged haphazardly in the dayroom with many patients seated with their back to the front. Participation was limited to a vociferous few and consisted of stereotyped complaints and/or demands for changes with much emphasis on better food and increased smoking privileges. Gradually more and more patients came to participate, including those very depressed or "deteriorated." At times long silent individuals would rise spontaneously to make some remarks or ask questions. There were occasional cross-discussions about "who should be admitted to the ward," or "should the television set be on during the day," or "should patients who persistently violate rules be transferred to a closed ward." Frequently the patients' recommendations were even more severe than those of the staff. Underlying psychopathologic trends were accentuated in these group interchanges, for patients would react in conformance with their psychotic symptomatology. Paranoid patients were always distrustful and suspicious, while severe schizophrenic and depressed patients sat the furthest away from the front of the room. The anxiety-ridden and agitated individuals would get up intermittently and pace the floor; the hallucinated might suddenly cry out in response to a voice; while the incoherent would rise to speak and then lapse into an unintelligible stream.

67

The meetings tended to reinforce the group spirit and many patients would defend another unjustly attacked. Each frequently reminded the other of their duties to the more unfortunate—the older and sicker people on the ward.

A feature of these meetings has been the discussion of patient notes put into the suggestion box. These ranged from accusations of stealing by other patients to denunciation of an attendant for alleged wrongs. Occasionally there were complaints of being "experimented upon," of being "forced to take medicine," or of being "kept in the hospital" unjustly. A vote was often taken to see what patient sentiment was regarding such inflammable issues. Eventually all of these questions were settled to the group's satisfaction. No patient has ever demanded a transfer because of the research nature of the ward, although everybody, including relatives, are aware of this fact. One patient who stated bitterly that she was "ready to go home but was being kept here" found no support among the others and never voiced the same complaint again. It was only after months that a relative feeling of freedom of expression existed. Obviously a long time will have to elapse before patients will cease to fear retaliation. Occasionally bitter criticism was voiced of the medical or nursing staff. This usually finished with "now go ahead and transfer me." Since this was not done, the hostility decreased progressively.

These meetings were an accurate mirror of staff indecision. When for various reasons some restrictive measures were being decided upon, i.e., transfer of unruly and unmanageable patients to a locked ward, the succeeding group meeting was noisy and full of complaints. Emphasis would usually be placed on the food, although everyone knew that this was quite satisfactory for a large institution. Inordinate and unrealistic demands would be made, and when ungratified would lead to further complaints. These meetings tended to last much longer than others. There are periods when the meetings are short and unproductive and these cycles are still inexplicable.

After the closed patients' meetings were introduced on Thursday morning, the number of notes in the suggestion box decreased since all potentially critical material was discussed in closed session by the patients and handed to the author in the form of minutes. Wherever possible, patient requests for improvement were acted upon. This gave a sense of reality to staff urgings for their participation.

THE STAFF MEETINGS

These were attended by the psychiatrists, nurses, practical nurses and attendants. At the outset, nursing staff displayed attitudes ranging from anxiety and fear, to outright hostility towards the therapeutic community. Questions such as, "What happens to us if a patient escapes," or "supposing the key is lost," were very frequent. It was extremely difficult to induce them to exert initiative or to suggest innovations in the established nursing procedures. Rebelliousness and hostility expressed itself usually by passive acceptance of all new ideas. This was, however, followed by gradually increased inertia and the projects eventually were abandoned. After three months in the face of an almost open rebellion, these meetings were suspended.

The proposed change from a locked to open service with complete shift in emphasis from an authoritarian restrictive attitude to one of moderate permissiveness, requiring greater initiative, creativeness and self-awareness, so endangered their defenses that it was felt wiser to abandon these discussions and delay the opening of the ward. Instead, individual meetings were held with different members of nursing staff. It became apparent after a while that they could not cope with medical staff demands, and that the latter's pace was much too rapid.

At the outset there was the problem of split authority with nursing supervisors capable of countermanding medical orders. This was solved by making all staff members of the research ward responsible only to the director of research.

PHYSICIANS' ATTITUDES

The physicians engaged in this study were, perhaps, more aware of the positive values of therapeutic community than of the larger number of difficult problems encountered in guiding such an operation. The ward could not exist as an isolated unit but functioned within the larger hospital structure subject to all of the potential stresses and strains. The medical personnel were thus in the center of pressures from some of the administrative staff not to disturb the status quo and prevent untoward episodes, while the patients were desirous of more and more liberties. Consequently it was necessary to adopt a very flexible attitude which changed with various events both in the ward and hospital at large.

There was frequent discord amongst the physicians concerning application of various therapies, permissiveness versus disciplinarian attitudes, attitudes towards nursing staff and the rest of the hospital, etc. These at times created a feeling of tension in the ward, and unfortunately it was not always possible to arrive at a consensus (14). Hostility of one physician to another would be expressed by countermanding orders, removing patients from study projects or by inattention to important administrative details.

DISCUSSION

Our observations during the past two years indicate the feasibility of operating a former continuous treatment ward with both very chronic and acutely ill female patients along the principles of a therapeutic community, even though innumerable problems are involved. Thirty-four patients were hospitalized from one to three years, and 20 patients five years or more (Table 3). Forty patients were 40 years or older. With more than 50% of patients in the moderate to severely chronic category and in the "over 40" age bracket, the holding of a group meeting with general participation was difficult. It would seem reasonable to assume that only the more recent and younger admissions would participate; a fact observable each week. Having emphasized the necessity of daily occupation, the lack of personnel seriously hampered drawing chronic patients into any meaningful activity. Personnel shortages will always make a therapeutic community difficult to operate, and recruitment must draw upon those individuals who have some technical skills. In spite of this, the high spirit of duty and devotion by the available staff succeeded in operating the workshop, occupational therapy on the ward, and other group activities.

The persistent complaints regarding food and smoking by the ward population would indicate marked needs for oral gratification with fixation and/or regression to this infantile level. The recrudescence of such complaints when the environment became threatening indicated the great difficulty these patients have in reality adjustment. Strong needs to be gratified, accepted and loved were always evident, and frustration was usually followed by hostility.

Every patient is not a candidate for participation in a therapeutic community. Some found the freedom too threatening and either directly asked for transfer to a locked ward ("It's dangerous to be here. The door is opened and somebody can walk in."), or else repeatedly committed infractions of ward rules necessitating their transfer. In most cases, external freedom threatened the rigid inner safeguards of their own hostility and aggression. Contrary to Hurst (15), we have not found that "deteriorated schizophrenics who have spent many years in the hospital provide most of the difficulty." The potential threat of violence never materialized, and actually decreased (16).

Infractions of the rules of conduct on the ward are dealt with after complete discussion between patients and the staff in the Wednesday morning meeting. It is necessary at times to restrict patients to the ward for short periods and even place them on a locked ward during the day. Punishment must be thoroughly explained and under such circumstances is almost always accepted. Patients felt the open ward gave them more liberty and there was no need to act out. One very agitated patient was taken for long walks about the grounds and thus handled successfully. The open door symbolized much of the ward operation and was looked upon by patients as one of the most significant events during the past two years (17). It must be emphasized strongly that the doors of any ward should not be opened unless preceded by a long indoctrination period. In addition, an intensive occupational therapy program must be in operation; otherwise patients merely walk about aimlessly.

By implication, Jacoby *et al.* (18), have suggested that sexual promiscuity is a problem in wards moving towards an open door or a therapeutic community. This had appeared to be the same here until these problems ceased following the departure of two staff members. There is no question that some patients with defective super-ego development will not perceive the social implications of their sexual "acting out." Yet, it is interesting to speculate whether or not unconscious projections by the staff may play some role.

Is an open door necessary for a therapeutic community? The affirmative is held here contrary to Rundle and Briggs (19), and Wilmer (20). The open door is perceived as the symbol of liberty and is inherently an expression of the "new order" in mental hospitals. To keep patients behind locked doors and barred windows makes the atmosphere prison-like irrespective of social interaction and daily or frequent ward meetings. Our operation may be criticized on the other hand, since the entire ward only met once weekly. However, the chronicity of our population would not make additional meetings profitable, and even here the hypothesis would have to be tested.

The issue of social therapy versus chemotherapy is far from settled. Jones (1) uses virtually no chemotherapy at Belmont. Yet it is difficult to compare his ward to ours, since we have a heterogeneous psychotic population. Racamier (12) has stated that the hospital can aggravate and complicate the schizophrenic psychosis and suggests that symptoms are induced by the hospital environment. Sher (21) feels that "relatively random and apparently disorganized behavior of the regressed schizophrenic particularly was a product of the structure of the hospital itself." Rathod (22), after an experimental study, believed that "intensive and varied occupational activities" may be responsible for patient improvement rather than the drugs.

My observations both abroad and in this country during the project indicate that generalizations and extrapolations from one culture to another cannot be made. Where the patient population is of a homogeneous ethnic group, as in some English hospitals, it may well be that drugs can be dispensed with in psychiatric treatment. However, when we are dealing with explosive, unpredictable personalities coming from heterogeneous national groups with poor social mores, defective concepts of self-discipline, and a virtually non-existent family unit, one finds the quantitative characteristics of the psychosis entirely different. While the very favorable social setting on the ward has permitted some involutional depressions to clear within several days without any treatment, we found the family in these cases to be the pathogenic agent. Removal of the patient to a supportive warm environment was therapeutic. On the other hand, most depressions required physiological or drug treatment.

We were successful in discharging one patient hospitalized 19 years after the resocialization and rehabilitation program had begun coupled with intensive chemotherapy using the newest psychopharmacologic agents available. Some regressed, incoherent patients have improved. One has been discharged, while two are preparing to leave. A detailed breakdown of this data will be reported subsequently. I firmly believe that the only effective treatment in this setting is a combination of intensive chemotherapy, psychotherapy and rehabilitation.

The staff problems seem crucial in a therapeutic community. Patients followed the progressive liberalization easily and without difficulty. It is absolutely essential that the nursing staff be properly indoctrinated at a *slow pace* before any doors are opened. So much anxiety and hostility was aroused towards the rapidity with which medical staff pushed this operation at the outset that the entire project was halted for a time. A therapeutic community cannot function unless the nurses and attendants are enthusiastically committed. This problem has been considered elsewhere (23).

73

Since the ward exists as part of a hospital, it is subject to many administrative procedures which can seriously handicap the daily operation. Many efforts were made to undercut this operation and finally these were circumvented by making the unit completely autonomous. While traditionally power in a state hospital is vested in the superintendent, it may be wise for others considering such procedures as therapeutic communities to have these powers delegated. The need to "be informed" has much basis in tradition, but may realistically tend to reduce the efficiency of ward operations.

It would seem that a therapeutic community should be conducted by individuals conversant with psychodynamic principles. The therapeutic community represents after all the involvement of innumerable personalities often with opposing points of view. Since staff indecision or antagonisms are easily and rapidly perceived by the patients, this must be dissolved before the repercussions are felt on the ward. One Wednesday meeting was featured by marked hostility to the psychiatrists. This was eventually traced to a markedly ambivalent staff attitude regarding transfers to other wards which created anxiety among the patients. They felt that this could be used as a thinly disguised form of punishment.

The leader of such a group must understand clearly the principles of a therapeutic community, the dynamic and very fluid relationship between medical, nursing staff and patients, both within themselves and to each other. Indecision may have disrupting effects upon group morale and create a vacuous state for the patients. On the other hand, once committed, this operation must be defended against all external disrupting forces. The freedom of the ward, its operations and its autonomy are bound to create hostility elsewhere in the institution. This sequence has been observed in other hospitals under similar conditions (24). Unfortunately, there is no easy solution to this complex problem.

One may ask what benefits have been derived from this project. The freedom of such a ward, the lack of restrictive, repressive and regressive measures, and the attention to small details of human

74

living have practically eliminated the destructive acting-out process. The ward has become a better place for the patients to live in, and the staff devotes all its energies to therapy. It no longer "watches" patients but "directs" them into activities designed to absorb their interests throughout the day. Observations are more complete and directed to the perception of psychopathologic findings rather than "when will she go off again." It may be that after a while patients will seek treatment much more quickly in case of relapse, since some have said, "If I get sick again, I'll never mind coming back here." Under intensive observation by the entire staff throughout the day, patients returned from convalescent status no longer are "lost" in the ward.

Intensive application of "the social approach" can increase the yield of improvement resulting from drugs alone. The former is, however, a long process and in the present case took two years. The importance of work therapy has already been considered elsewhere (11).

SUMMARY

The operation, problems, and analysis of results during a two year operation of the therapeutic community of the research division at Manhattan State Hospital with acute and chronic patients has been described.

CONCLUSIONS

1. It is possible to operate a chronic ward with acute patients as a therapeutic community.

2. The open door is a symbol of this ward.

3. Long intensive indoctrination of nursing staff with adequate occupational therapy must precede opening the door.

4. Cultural differences do not permit easy translation of similar operations elsewhere to this country.

5. It is advisable that new admissions to such a ward be made slowly—no more than two per week.

6. While social factors are important in psychopathology, they cannot be singled out as the determining factors. Adequate treatment in present day psychiatry must integrate all therapies available without particular or unique emphasis on any one.

75

ACKNOWLEDGMENT

Such a project would have been impossible without the unstinting devotion of the entire ward staff under the direction of Miss D. Kaufmann, R. N.

BIBLIOGRAPHY

1. Denber, H. C. B.: Personal observations.

2. Walk, A.: Some aspects of the "Moral Treatment" of the insane up to 1854. *J. Ment. Sci., 100:* 807, 1954.

3. Jones, M.: The treatment of personality disorders in a therapeutic community. *Psychiatry, 20:* 211, 1957.

4. Wilmer, H. A.: Psychiatric therapeutic community in a naval hospital. *J.A.M.A., 166:* 1445, (March 22) 1958.

5. Greenblatt, M., Levinson, D. J., and Williams, R. H.: The patient and the mental hospital. Illinois, The Free Press, 1957.

6. Hardgrove, T. J., and Schlosser, J. R.: What is a therapeutic community? *Mental Hospitals, 8:* 14, 1957.

7. Cumming, E., and Cumming, J.: The locus of power in a large mental hospital. *Psychiatry, 19:* 351, 1956.

8. Pollak, O.: Staff discomforts and the social organization of a mental hospital. *Psychiatry, 19:* 309, 1956.

9. In the Mental Hospital. London, The Lancet, 1955.

10. Organisation du Travail Thérapeutique Dans les Hôpitaux Psychiatriques. Paris, Ministère de la Santé Publique, (February 4) 1958.

11. Denber, H. C. B.: Work therapy for psychiatric patients. *Mental Hospitals,* in press.

12. Racamier, P. C.: Introduction à une sociopathologie des schizophrènes hospitalisés. *L'Evolution Psychiatrique, 1:* 47, 1957.

13. Charatan, F. B., Denber, H. C. B., and Travis, J. H.: A method for accelerating discharge from state hospitals. *Amer. J. Psychiat., 114:* 939, 1958.

14. Stanton, A. H., and Schwartz, M. S.: The mental hospital. New York, Basic Books, 1954.

15. Hurst, L.C.: The unlocking of wards in mental hospitals. *Amer. J. Psychiat., 114:* 306, 1957.

16. Mandelbrote, B.: An experiment in the rapid conversion of a closed mental hospital into an open-door hospital. *Mental Hygiene, 42:* 3, 1958.

17. Wisebord, N., Denber, H. C. B., Charatan, F. B., and Travis, J. H.: Patients reactions to the "open door." *Amer. J. Psychiat., 115:* 518, 1958.

18. Jacoby, M. G., Babikian, H., McLamb, E., and Hohlbein, B.: A study in non-restraint. *Amer. J. Psychiat., 115:* 114, 1958.

19. Rundle, F. L., and Briggs, D. L.: Beginnings of a therapeutic community. *U. S. Armed Forces Med. J., 8:* 811, 1957.

20. Wilmer, H. A.: Toward a definition of the therapeutic community. *Amer. J. Psychiat., 114:* 824, 1958.

21. Scher, J. M.: The structured ward: Research method and hypothesis in a total treatment setting for schizophrenia. *A.M.A. Arch. Neurol. Psychiat., 78:* 531, 1957.

22. Rathod, N. H.: Tranquilisers and patients' environment. *The Lancet, 1:* 611, (March 22) 1958.

23. Kauffman, D., and Denber, H. C. B.: A nurse looks at therapeutic community. Neuro-Psychopharmacology, Amsterdam, Elsevier, 1959. In press.

24. Schlosser, J. R.: Personal communication.

DISCUSSION OF DR. DENBER'S PAPER

Dr. Leigh M. Roberts:—

The role of staff attitudes in working toward a ward therapeutic community is well presented by Dr. Denber and similar to the attitudes of personnel experienced in many other hospitals as this type of therapy was innovated. It is difficult for patients and staff members to accept altered roles as a ward moves from the physician's domain to the patient's domain. Similarly, changes occur from an essentially passive to an active patient role wherein patients are no longer passively treated by the staff but they exert a significant influence on their environment. The best and worst qualities of the personnel are often quickly exposed when patients are asked along with the personnel to participate in environmental therapy. The threat evoked by such exposition provides many opportunities and necessities for working with the staff.

These changes culminate in alterations of ward policy and organization with blurring of hierarchical status lines. The staff members lose some of the protection of this structure as they are asked to adopt therapeutic attitudes in interpersonal relationships with the patients and other staff members. Such developments arouse anxiety in the personnel who may respond with either active or passive resistance to the contemplated changes. The open management and discussion of such resistances provide one of the keys to the success of the initiation of a therapeutic community. The described resistance has been repeated in nearly every development of a therapeutic community to varying degrees. The enhancement of free communication at all levels is one of the means of dealing with it most effectively.

The function of the nurse in charge of the ward needs close scrutiny. As the individual who assumes responsibility for all members of the ward staff and the effectiveness of their functioning, as the person who is responsible to the physician in charge to carry out his desires, and as the one to whom patients may turn with their dissatisfactions, she is caught in a multidirectional crossfire with conflicting demands placed on her. The need for a flexible energetic person with enthusiasm for interpersonal relationships in this role is evident as the stress is great. Similarly, there may be profound need for the ward physician to emotionally support this individual if she is to function effectively.

The leadership of the ward physician is also an important factor in development of a therapeutic community. The inertia provided by the changed role of patients and the resistance of staff members to evolve a program conducive to activating patient's problems instead of repressing them results in a need for the physician to offer guidance, leadership and a continuous emotional investment or the program functions below its optimal therapeutic capacity. This type of program is difficult to evolve in most state hospitals to the point where it is self-perpetuating without the continuous energetic leadership of one or a few persons. This appears to be historically one of the factors in the disintegration of earlier somewhat similar humanitarian institutional reform movements

A SELF-CONTAINED WOMEN'S WARD
AS A THERAPEUTIC COMMUNITY

G. J. Sarwer-Foner, M. D.,
W. Ogle, M. D.,
T. E. Dancey, M. D.

INTRODUCTION

People have certain social needs, both when ill or well. When well they need a sense of personal integrity and adequacy. At the level of human relationships, these are demonstrated by social signs. Among these are the feeling of being accepted and of being looked upon favorably by environmental figures important to the individual. This is accompanied by the feeling that they have a place; that what they are and what they do is recognized and has some favorable status—in short, a feeling of belonging and a sense of prestige. All interpersonal contacts occur at an emotional level around the presence or absence of these factors, and around conflicts to establish, and strivings to attain such acceptance for the individual.

People with physical illnesses have to be able to lie back, regress, and allow others to care for them; feeling confident that they will receive the care they need to get well. People suffering from psychiatric illnesses have always had various degrees of trauma to their self-esteem, have wondered about their own worth, their own identities in terms of who they are, and what they are. They tend to devaluate their own powers and capacities, have no confidence in their own ability to face up to things or to master their own problems.

These doubts are based on real experiences in the past life, and had given rise to doubts at a deeper feeling level as to whether they are able to achieve, through their own strivings and by their own worth, those goals of acceptance and recognition, with the accompanying feelings of adequacy and prestige.

The hospital is supposed to be a place where people can get well, and where their needs can be met. It should also foster the development of the attitudes that his or her problems are human and can be dealt with at this level. Hospitals should create the attitude that through his own efforts, with the aid of doctors and nurses, the patient can master the illness which represents impulses in him that he can no longer face or handle. Implicit in all that has been said so far is the attitude that the hospital will help the person feel more like an acceptable human being.

81

In order to do this, it must be organized so as not to strip the individual of his "dignity." One may ask what "human dignity" means? The patient who comes to the hospital for treatment feels that he is a person, while his rights as an individual are never questioned. The attitudes about the person's individuality should be so firmly fixed within the structure and framework of the hospital that there can be no question in the patient's or in the staff's mind. This reflects an underlying attitude of the entire hospital hierarchical organization expressed at all levels of feeling and thinking and, therefore, creates a hospital effluvium, or atmosphere, perceived and felt at all levels by the patient. *This is the milieu.* The type of patient concerned, and the type of hospital framework organized, determines to a large degree the details of how this attitude is expressed and conveyed to the patient.

The treatment philosophy of the planning staff is obviously a most important factor in helping to determine both the type of patient accepted for treatment, as well as the way in which this would be done.

It is obvious that the type of hospital establishment one designs is dependent on the specific needs of the patient group. In our case, this consisted largely of single young women with a sprinkling of middle-aged, married, and elderly women of the veterans group; many would be members of the Canadian Armed Services. All would either be serving Naval, Military, or Air Force personnel, or eligible veterans of World Wars I and II. Consideration of the entire situation led us to feel that the best possible treatment for their neurotic problems, or those types of psychotic disturbances best handled in an open setting, would be in an open treatment facility with psychoanalytically oriented psychotherapy as the principal approach. Other treatments would be used within this framework, so that ECT, sub-coma insulin, CO_2, nitrous oxide and others including neuroleptic drugs (when they later became available), would be used as the need arose.

The physical aspects of the unit were designed to give each patient a feeling that she was "at home," with a living area of her

82

own, a bed, and a place for clothes. Adequate housekeeping facilities, a day room and an integrated program of activities were planned.

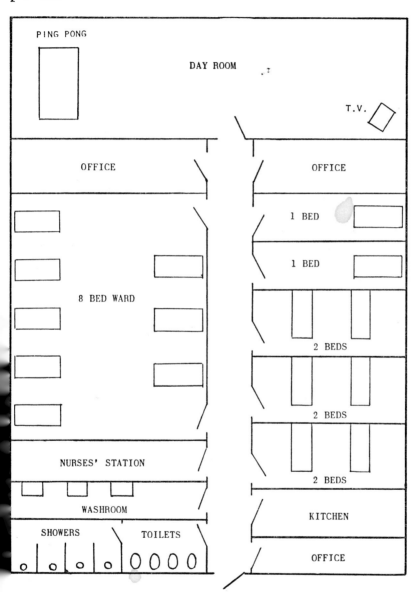

FIGURE 1—Physical organization of ward.

It is obviously the ward staff that largely determines the treatment philosophy. The man in charge of the actual program necessarily sets the tone and operational level of the department. Because of this, from the very onset it was felt necessary for the treating personnel to have the clearest understanding of the policy, philosophy and organization of the unit. A series of discussions were held, with directives and orders on policy matters set forth by the Psychiatrist-in-Chief. A clear-cut hierarchy was established as shown in Figure II.

LINES of AUTHORITY and COMMUNICATION

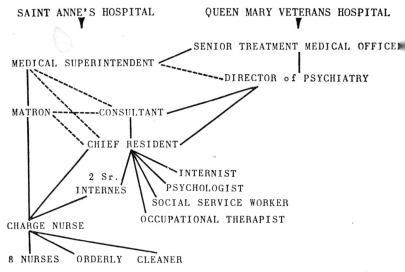

FIGURE 2—Solid lines are primary, and dotted lines are secondary lines of authority and communication.

In this regard it is important to note that the main source of administrative authority was the Psychiatrist-in-Chief of the Queen Mary Veterans Hospital going to the Unit Consultant and thence to the Chief Resident. Subordinate lines of communication existed directly between the Resident and the Psychiatrist-in-Chief, since the former was the Resident-in-Chief at both Queen Mary Veterans Hospital and the special unit at Ste. Anne

84

Hospital, and was thus in very close over-all administrative touch. The same clarity of administrative hierarchy and lines of communication for discussion, both of clinical material and of any problems that might arise, existed within the treatment team.

The latter formed a harmonious group, meeting often in formal sessions to discuss clinical material, and in weekly conferences with the Consultant for teaching and administrative purposes. The staff conferences fulfilled multiple roles for both the Consultant and the Resident. It served for clinical discussions, and as the rallying point for the treatment team where the reports of the occupational therapists, psychologists, social workers, and treating physicians were discussed.

The staff often dined together and discussed many things of clinical interest. As a result of this good group relationship, a healthy attitude developed amongst the staff, and as a result the same atmosphere was created between staff and patients.

ORGANIZATION OF THE WOMEN'S UNIT

Female patients eligible for treatment in a Federal Government Hospital had been admitted for psychiatric treatment to a women's ward for medical, surgical and selected psychiatric cases at Queen Mary Veterans Hospital since the inception of its Department of Psychiatry. The desirability of establishing a special facility for those who might need continuous treatment resulted in the Psychiatrist-in-Chief, Dr. T. E. Dancey, arranging for a 16-bed, open, self-contained treatment facility to be established at the Ste. Anne's Veterans Hospital, some 20 miles from Montreal. In outlining details of the principles and philosophy behind this establishment, the first word that deserves important consideration is the word "open." How does one make a person feel that she will, through her own efforts and with some help from the hospital, conquer and overcome whatever problems beset her? In order to attempt this and remain "open," the following criteria must exist, and all planning be based on these straightforward sociological and psychological facts.

85

The ward should act as a good surrogate of the family group which will correct some of the previous wrongdoings and injustices. In order to fulfill these functions, it must be based on the following:

1. Patients who show homicidal or suicidal behavior cannot be admitted, nor can those who will wreck the furniture, or otherwise destroy the unit; patients who will use the ward as a base for disorderly operations which the community as a whole or the hospital administration cannot tolerate, such as getting drunk on the ward, cashing bad checks, using either narcotics or medication obtained from non-hospital sources, cannot be treated either. The patient should be able to remain in the treatment setting voluntarily. A limited amount of departing from the hospital grounds without permission can be tolerated, if it occurs in a specific "testing-out" psychotherapeutic sense. The tolerance of a unit to this is usually small.

2. Any patient, regardless of diagnosis, who does not violate the above principles can be treated in an open hospital with hope and success. Certain patients who do not respect the above can be treated in a closed ward.

3. Attitudes to authority are usually initially based on past reality experiences. A major part of this initial reality involved the attitudes of the parents. This was then projected on to future contacts with organizations of hierarchical nature.

Based on the above-mentioned needs of an open hospital, our attitude was that a patient had all the rights and freedoms that she would have in a well-organized family home. This was applied within the framework of the hospital organization.

Any objections to a regimen on a patient's part could be discussed with her doctor. Thus, meal hours were set just as in a family group. If patients were well enough, they were given permission to come and go as they pleased, but had to tell the nurse where they were going and when they would return. They had to be in for meal hours unless arranged for otherwise. Bedtime hour was fixed, but provided they did not interfere with others, patients could within the confines of their own rooms sleep, read, or engage in other activities. If they were too ill for freedom of movement, the physicians and nurses would explain this, discussing any objections. The patients had to dress after a certain hour in the morning for entry to the general ward areas, i.e., outside their rooms. If they wished to remain in pajamas or bathrobe, or to remain in their rooms, this was permissible, but became, like all behavior, a subject for psychotherapeutic exchange. The staff attitude about this was that in their own domain the patients could do as they wished, but when they came into contact with other patients, they had to please them to some degree, as well as not violate other people's rights. There was no pressure as to how they dressed beyond this.

Behavior when on weekend pass, or when out of the hospital, was their own affair. Implicit was, however, the very strong feeling that their behavior could not bring disgrace or reflect badly, administratively, socially, or legally on the hospital, any more than the family unit would want the actions of one of its members to bring social disgrace upon it.

STRUCTURE OF THE WARD

It was a 16-bed ward for female patients, located within the confines of the 1,335-bed veterans' hospital for chronic, medical, surgical and psychiatric diseases. It was the only active treatment ward for non-chronic illness in this part of the hospital. Although part of St. Anne's Veterans' Hospital, it was administratively under the control of the Department of Psychiatry, Queen Mary Veterans Hospital. It had a head nurse of its own, and a total complement of eight nurses assigned from Ste. Anne's for the 24 hours. It was thus arranged that six nurses were on duty each day. This was a much higher nurse-patient ratio than existed in the rest of Ste. Anne's. Many patients were admitted with psychosomatic difficulties, conversion symptoms, or psychophysiological reactions such as headache, nausea, fainting spells, abdominal cramps. Marked anxiety and bouts of depression were common. Acute schizophrenic and psychotic depressive episodes were also seen. Secondary alcoholism with some acting-out behavior was sometimes seen. Treatment time was usually limited to three or four months of in-patient treatment, so that psychoanalysis was neither the aim nor a possibility. Rather, reconstruction of ego-supportive defenses, through increased confidence in their own acceptability, and living through of an experience in which they were treated as human beings, was the focus of the unit.

The ward population had a high proportion of adolescent young girls in their late teens and early twenties, who had volunteered for services in the R.C.A.F., usually learning specific Air Force Trades. Ten were in their teens, 23 were in their twenties, 11 in their thirties, and two in their forties. Two patients were in their fifties or sixties. The majority were enlisted as radar or electronic technicians. There were also some Airwomen police, stenographers, and special trades. Many of these would be sent to us for treatment after varying periods of service. The feeling of not belonging, the problem of adjusting to service life, the change in sexual mores seen in some cases, the problems of barrack-room life, isolated stations, boredom, monotony, prolonged contact with people of the same sex, the predominantly large groups of women with relatively few men (many of whom were married), the exacting repetitive work demanded of some, the use of alcohol to channelize anxiety and symptoms—all these formed part of the sociological context from which the different patients came. Interpersonal difficulties, conflicts about hierarchy, struggles about feelings of acceptance or rejection, recognition, frustration, ambivalence about psychosexual development, about their roles as females, were also seen.

Six patients were treated for less than one month; 14 for one to two months; 15 for two to three months; nine for three to four months; two for four to five months, and three from six to seven months. Thus, the majority were treated from one to three months.

PHYSICAL ORGANIZATION

The physical plant consisted of three offices (Figure I), one of which was the main office for the physicians. Separated from the nursing station and the large ward, by a corridor, were five rooms, three of which could be used as two-bed rooms, while the remaining two were one-bed rooms. One of the two-bed rooms was used as a treatment room for ECT. On the other side of the corridor there was an eight-bed ward. In the morning this ward was used as a sub-coma insulin unit, when needed. Those patients who happened to sleep there, but were not being given sub-coma insulin, would leave this area during the morning sub-coma insulin.

At the end of the hall was a large room used as a day and dining room, with a TV set, radio and record player, as well as a ping-pong table. A large table, which was a communal dining table, was also present. This room served for selected O. T. activities and as a general living room. A kitchen, utility, washroom, cupboards, bathrooms, and a washing and ironing room for patients were part of the unit.

The area was entered through a door opening onto the main hospital cross-corridor. The hospital recreational and occupational facilities included a bowling alley, a nine-hole golf course, a beach, and a swimming area; an excellent patients' library, gym, excellent facilities for occupational therapy, a physiotherapy unit, a large recreational hall, spacious grounds, and a Canadian Red Cross lounge for the reception of visitors. The hospital supplied the usual medical and surgical departments, laboratories, and x-rays, with all consultants and auxiliary personnel.

COMPOSITION OF TREATMENT TEAM

The man in charge of the department necessarily sets the tone for the group. How he feels about the attitudes and the policies under which he must operate determines to some degree how he reacts, and how he, therefore, organizes the work. The manner in which he visualizes how he is open to attack, or conversely to protection by his superiors on certain policy matters, determines to a large degree his feelings of security. If given the assurance that his superiors will respect, and expect him to respect his patients as individual human beings, variable treatment frameworks and attitudes can then exist. Which ones are selected and used depend on his personality, training and attitudes. In order to function successfully, he must feel that his efforts to treat the patients will win recognition and respect, will not bring him into remarkable conflict with his superiors, and as a result they will offer administrative support.

His subordinate physicians will take their cues from him in all these areas. They will either then tend to please him or subtly rebel against him. These phenomena are always secondary to the attitudes he conveys about what he wishes them to do with the patients, and also to his own interpersonal relations with them.

The nurses need to feel that they are supported. They will respond to the attitudes set by the physician as to discipline and the limits placed on the patients' general behavior. Nurses must not feel that they are being placed in equivocal situations with their own superiors (the hospital matron, or directoress of nurses), who have transcending authority. This independent and transcending authority could conceivably be used to intervene between the ward nurses' relationship with their immediate medical superiors in the Psychiatric Unit. How the nurses feel about their superiors, the physicians, and the patients, creates further currents of agreement or discord within this framework.

The manner in which the other professional personnel—resident staff, psychologists, social workers, occupational therapists, physical training instructors, librarians, orderlies, cleaners—are used within the treatment facility depends to a large degree on the prevailing attitude of the "man-in-charge." This would include his visualizations of teaching, interpersonal relations, and the treatment philosophy.

As a general rule, the smaller the unit, the more intense the relationships, the greater the harmony or disharmony, and the more subtle and powerful the various currents and undercurrents that pass between various staff members and patients. Rivalries for positions, likes, dislikes, and possible unconscious scapegoating (by that is meant the selection of one member of the staff to blame for much that may go wrong in the unit) have all often been described. These phenomena often have greater intensity in small groups.

What permitted the unit being described to avoid most of the above-mentioned pitfalls was the clear-cut policy decisions from the chief. These operated through the well defined lines of both authority and intracommunication on all matters. Part and parcel of this was an attitude which encouraged close interpersonal contacts and open discussions of difficulties as they arose.

The Chief Resident in psychiatry would be in his fifth year of post-graduate training. He was the person who directed the treatment and who, in practice, set much of the basic atmosphere of the ward. Superior to him was the Consultant. This Consultant represented the over-all administrative authority for the unit. Working with the Chief Resident would be a team composed of one or more senior interns, each with two or three years of psychiatric experience. Another senior intern from the Mental Infirmary, Ste. Anne's Hospital, or a rotator from the Medical Service, seconded to psychiatry for a period of up to four months, might also be attached to the unit for varying periods.

A vital part of the organization was the hospital nursing staff. This consisted of the chief nurse, whose attitudes, and respect for the human dignity of the patients was vital to the functioning of the unit. She was also, to a large degree, responsible for inculcating into subordinate nurses, and even new internes, the prevailing attitudes and treatment procedures. This was most important because the daily hour-to-hour interpretation of the established rules and regulations depended more upon the nurses, who dealt with the patients on the 24 hour-a-day basis, than on the doctors who were there for a fragment of this time.

All patients received psychological tests. Two and sometimes three psychologists worked as part of the treatment team.

One to two social workers were attached to the unit and saw all patients. Routine family, or social histories were always obtained, and contacts with administrative personnel at a patient's military unit, or with the patient's family were always carried out through the social workers. They formed a most invaluable portion of the team.

The occupational therapists played a vital role in the program. One or more were assigned and carried out all procedures, both recreational and occupational, swimming, boating, bowling, other athletic activities or handicrafts. The choice of programs was wide. The reports of the occupational therapists about the attitudes and participation of patients and on the patient's socialization, gave much valuable information.

TEACHING AND CONFERENCES

The entire treatment team met in once weekly conferences with the Consultant. The entire staff attended, with the occupational therapists, psychologists, and often visitors from other departments. These sessions were important for the teaching program. Discussions of the psychotherapy, diagnosis, administrative and other problems were thrashed out at these meeting sessions which would last one to three hours.

The ward had been established 15 months prior to the year's functioning (1954-55) that forms the basis of this paper.*

In the year described here, one of us (W. O.) lived at Ste Anne's and visited the ward for several hours daily (morning and night). In addition to this, the treating physician would commute from Q.M.V.H. three days a week.

For night emergencies, or on days when the treatment staff were not actually present at Ste. Anne's, the resident and specialist staff of Ste. Anne's Veterans Hospital were available. But before any psychiatric procedures, other than emergency medica or life saving procedures, could be carried out, the psychiatric

---

* Dr. C. C. Smith was the first resident and helped establish the first treatmen team. Dr. S. Wilner was the first consultant to the unit. Dr. Smith was consultan for the one year period of this study.

staff had to be contacted by telephone. Here lay an administrative loophole which was impossible to block, since an inexperienced non-psychiatric medical or surgical intern or nurse might well react differently to a ward situation than the better psychiatrically oriented psychiatric personnel. This arrangement, nevertheless, worked remarkably well in practice.

TREATMENT PROGRAM

The treatment program, for the first 15 months of the unit's existence, consisted of a total push centered on psychoanalytically oriented psychotherapy, but with the already described ancillary treatments. All received some sort of psychotherapy. Sub-coma insulin, ECT, and those tranquilizing drugs available at the time (reserpine and chlorpromazine) were used when necessary. The indications for organic therapies were drastically limited, and they were used adjunctively. The 16 patients were divided amongst the treating doctors. The Resident often treated the more difficult cases, because of his somewhat greater experience. Patients were seen in twice or thrice weekly sessions, usually lasting 45 minutes to an hour, unless there was a special reason for a shorter session. Some very ill patients sometimes could not tolerate longer periods at the beginning without becoming anxious.

Patients were referred to the unit only after having been seen by consultants, who assessed their state and determined their suitability for hospitalization. Psychological tests, contacts with social workers and occupational therapists, as well as explanation of ward procedures by the nursing staff were routine matters on admission. Group therapy was another important aspect of the treatment program. All able to attend were encouraged to do so. These meetings were held once or twice weekly for one to one-and-a-half hours. A psychologist and the two doctors concerned always sat in. One of the physicians acted as a group leader, while the other was an observer, and at times served as a focus for problems involving his own patients. The mere presence of their own doctor contributed much to the meaning of the sessions. Private aspects of problems would be referred for more intensive exploration with their own therapists.

Group therapy sessions were used for assessing patient interaction, for setting a common tone to general problems. Acting-out patients, those who were timid with difficulties in verbalization, or who felt that only they suffered in a particular manner, often gained from these meetings in which they heard others who had similar problems begin to solve them. Friendships, attractions, repulsions, hostilities, all were reflected here, often with greater clarity than in individual psychotherapy. The usual problems that one finds in group therapy arose, and balancing the composition of the group was always something of a challenge. Attempts must be made to encourage proper use and development of her own innate capacities, to conquer problems and meet people with lessened neurotic distortions, and better testing of motivations in a reality context. The recognition and expression of biological, social and human needs have to be part of this milieu.

DISCUSSION

What is done is more important than what is said. It is not sufficient to speak of a patient using his ability to face people and work out problems in psychotherapy if the ward unit fails to foster self-development by its daily organization and routine. If there is a violation of the latter principle, much petty acting-out against authority can occur, and these are usually expressions of resentment against the contradictions between what is said, what one means to do, and what one is actually doing. Recognition and correction of conflicting regulations helps settle such problems. The nurses at staff discussions were aware of this. Our nurses were remarkable in their ability to cooperate, to make the patients feel that the ward was their home while they were getting well, and they could behave in it with the complete freedom of a good home.

Admission policies, rules, and regulations should be based on solid facts and social realities. Patients with marked anti-social

94

tendencies cannot be treated in an open setting. Special facilities with a large patient-staff ratio are needed. The chief authority on the ward established the tone of the unit. He must be clear in his own mind about respecting human dignity and the rights of other professional people who use their own skills as part of the program. Open channels of communication must be established about problems, while good morale and rapport should exist. The chief should not attack the personalities of his co-workers nor should he treat them as though they were patients, but should always deal with the problems of the patients that provoked the personal reaction within the professional personnel. Lines of communication and authority must be sharp and clearly defined.

The medical authority must be paramount on the ward, and the authority of the senior medical person must be clearly established. In order to do this successfully, the approval by the higher authorities of the policies under which the therapeutic community is operating must be implicit and, when necessary, explicit. Any conflicts about this are automatically reflected in discord and administrative difficulty. Good liaison with the nursing office must exist in the organization because they had, in the unit described, much independent authority.

Jealousies, power struggles, sibling rivalries, likes or dislikes between members of the staff often cannot be dealt with at the level of discussion. The superior staff understood that these existed, and by keeping lines of administrative communication open, some help was given in their solution. At best, this remains a constant problem in any project of this type.

CONCLUSION

The principles demonstrated in the analysis of a year's functioning of this unit can be applied in varying degrees to any unit. The details will vary according to the type of hospital (open or closed), the patients, and the ward structure to be established. The group relations among the staff remain one of the crucial points in such an operation.

ACKNOWLEDGMENT

Though others worked with us from time to time, the following personnel were a consistent part of the treatment team during the year described in this paper. Our thanks are due to them for their collaboration: Internist, G. Neiman, M. D.; charge nurse, Miss Beaumont; psychologists, Miss A. Cousineau, Mr. W. B. Rankin; social service workers, Mrs. J. I. Kennett, Mrs. F. Cordeau, Mrs. Banfy; occupational therapist, Miss Y. Richards.

THE OPEN DOOR:
A STUDY OF INSTITUTIONAL CHANGE

Milton Greenblatt, M. D.,
Daniel J. Levinson, Ph.D.

—

INTRODUCTION

Today, many mental hospitals are making vigorous attempts to alter the physical and social environment for better patient care and treatment. One of the most dramatic changes has been the opening of doors giving patients greater freedom of movement and a sense of contact with the outside world. This has been hailed as a major forward step in the advance from custodial to therapeutic methods of patient care; yet at this date vast numbers of doors still remain closed. Are the risks and difficulties of the open door so great as to discourage mental hospital administrators? Is the continuation of a closed door policy to be attributed to organizational or administrative inertia?

In the hope of discovering answers to such questions, we have examined in detail the effects on our hospital of two attempts to open the last closed door in our adult patient section. The many issues and problems associated with these attempts are peculiarly suited to point up crucial conflicts between custodial and therapeutic philosophies.

THE HOSPITAL MILIEU:
CONTEXT FOR THE OPEN DOOR EXPERIMENTS

To a large extent the effects on hospital life of institutional change, such as the open door, depend on the kind of physical and social organization in which the change takes place. The Massachusetts Mental Health Center (located in an urban neighborhood, 10 minutes from downtown Boston) is an intensive treatment, teaching and research institution of relatively small size (approximately 130 in-patients at the time of the study) with a high staff-patient ratio, an eclectic treatment philosophy, and large training and research divisions. There is emphasis on a wide spectrum of therapies with dynamically oriented psychotherapy the chief modality, plus concentration on long-term relationships made possible by special out-patient and ex-patient services and day hospital facility. One of the principal research and therapeutic interests has been experiments with new methods of patient care through social-environmental changes or repatterning.

99

The growth of the Center as a therapeutic community since 1943 has been stimulated by many changes in its physical and social ecology. These have been detailed by Greenblatt, York and Brown (1). During this period the doors between the wards and the outside world have been opened one by one, so that by 1954 only one remained closed. This door connects a large day room or lounge for patients with the stairwell and elevator leading directly to the outside. The day room connects Ward 4 (newly-admitted men) and Ward 5 (newly-admitted women),

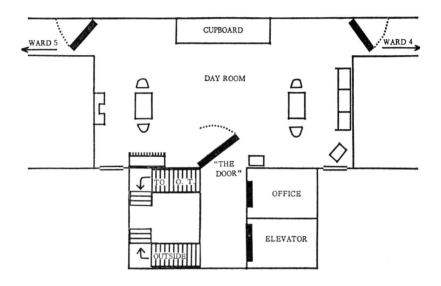

PHYSICAL LAYOUT SURROUNDING "THE DOOR"

both 30-35 bed dormitories. Each group has access to this day room. Among the changes that many of the staff have regarded as "gains" towards a more therapeutic community have been the opening of the doors connecting the two wards with this day room, so that both men and women patients may mingle freely, play cards, talk, watch television, or dance. But egress from the day room to the outside was up to the time of the study blocked by a heavy closed door.

This "last closed door" was a thorn in the side of the administration. An open door symbolized for them a freer environment for patients and represented an important stimulus and challenge to staff to manage patients by improved interpersonal relationships rather than by physical barriers. However, this view was not shared fully by psychiatric, nursing and other staff. Attempts to open this last closed door elicited all the resistances to change that may inhere in a complex social system. The "groans and pangs" of this social organism in its attempt to assimilate (or to sabotage) changes regarded as "progress" by administration, we believe, are of interest to those of us who are responsible for patient care in an institutional setting. In our hospital, opening the door was regarded as a major landmark in the hospital's history as well as an event of major consequence to patient welfare. (At the time this venture was first tried, there was no other hospital known to us in the United States with all its doors open.*)

We chronicle herein two experiments in opening the door—one that failed and one that succeeded. The first began in December 1954; the door was opened essentially through administrative fiat, remained open intermittently for some months and then was closed. Our understanding of this experiment is based mostly on retrospective data colored by the imperfections of recall. The second experiment took place in December 1956, approximately two years later. On this we have more reliable information based on attendance at conferences, interviewing personnel close to the scene, and on-the-spot observations. Although the door was occasionally closed by staff on some "emergency" basis, the second experiment soon "took" and the open door became assimilated into the social organism, not as a noxious foreign element, but as a healthy and vital aspect of its ongoing life.

THE FIRST EXPERIMENT

Some valuable lessons were learned from the first attempt to open the "last closed door" in December 1954. Some of the atti-

---

* We refer here to adult wards only. Our children's ward continues to have closed doors.

tudes preceding the event are mirrored in the Minutes of the Patient Government Meeting, November 18, 1954:

"President raised the question whether the members of Patient Government would like to have Wards 4 and 5 opened (to the outside). The members wanted to know how the few disturbed patients would be handled. Would they be allowed off the wards? It was felt that this would be left to the discretion of the doctors. After thought and observation, the members felt that most of the patients on these wards were cooperative and good subjects for an open ward. It was generally agreed to lift restrictions, have unlocked doors and give freedom to purchase cigarettes. A vote was taken to have Wards 4 and 5 opened under a monitored system. This decision was met with great enthusiasm. The request was forwarded to the assistant superintendent for approval."

He responded with a letter read at a subsequent meeting (December 2, 1954):

"I am very glad to hear you have been discussing the possibility of opening Wards 4 and 5. You bring up exactly the same problems as the hospital staff have been considering—how the few disturbed patients would be handled. Also would they be allowed off the wards?

Of course, this is not only a problem of the doctors but perhaps of whether sufficient nursing care can be provided so that someone could pay particular attention to these people. There is the further possibility that if there wasn't sufficient nursing personnel, patients could take some responsibility for those who were sicker than themselves.

Don't anticipate changes in this direction too soon; we still have quite a lot of figuring out how to avoid any difficulties that might arise well in advance."

The assistant superintendent's final caution is perhaps the clue to the anticipations and expectations of staff as well as patients. Since these wards housed the sickest patients as well as court cases and were often the scene of severe behavioral outbreaks, there was considerable apprehension concerning opening of this door. Moreover, the staff possessed meager knowledge about how the doors had been opened successfully in other places.

102

RETROSPECTIVE IMPRESSIONS AND ATTITUDES CONCERNING THE OPEN DOOR

For our picture of staff attitudes and reactions at that time we rely on retrospective information obtained some two years later in interviews with 30 staff members—nine nurses, five attendants, three occupational therapists, three social workers, five psychiatrists, one male supervisor, one technician, two clerks, and one secretary. Of these, 28 had been working in the hospital at the time of the original experiment; two had come to the hospital afterwards.

During the first experiment, the doors had been open for six months, from December to May; however, the survey two years later elicited diverse memories as to how long the doors really had remained open. Among the doctors interviewed the time was given in terms of months, while nurses, aides, O. T. workers, and social workers generally remembered it in terms of a couple of weeks to two months.

One attendant stated that the superintendent ordered them open as an experiment, "something for people to talk about when things are quiet in the hospital."

The recreational therapist said there had been no orders to open or close the doors, that it came as a *suggestion*. It was instigated because of the hospital's reputation for being progressive, an "open door" institution. This reputation had to be upheld.

Two of the social workers stated that the program was initiated through a direct order from the superintendent and assistant superintendent. One of them related an incident which she felt contributed to this decision: Officials from a mental hospital where the "open door policy" was already in practice had visited our hospital and had wondered why this hospital was not also following an open door policy.

Some attendants recalled that they did not like to be stationed at the open door. It was "too much like police work" and they felt like "human doors." It was too much responsibility; assignments were vague, and the man at the door drained the ward of needed personnel. Two attendants remarked that police

103

complained because of excess work imposed in retrieving escaped patients. Attendants complained that they were continually chasing after patients; more escapes would have been recorded except that "we were dragging them back from the stairs all day." One commented that those patients who escaped during the time when the doors were open were not the ones who "jimmied" locks and made other attempts to escape when the doors were locked. One female attendant recalled a meeting held with the patients on the wards in which "50 per cent of the patients admitted that they felt more secure with the doors closed, especially patients on ECT."

An O. T. worker emphasized the problems with court cases and remarked that the court did not like the idea of open wards. In contrast, the hospital male supervisor said that court cases gave the least trouble and were often the most helpful on the wards.

The chief of service felt that ward management had been less effective with open doors. Locked doors had given the personnel a "lever" over the patients so that, for example, an effective schedule could be arranged for patients to go back and forth to O. T. "With the open door," he said, "there was turmoil and disorganization with the patients leaving and returning to the ward . . . Because the open door gave the impression of continuity of the inside with the outside, many patients felt insecure and unsettled."

Several nurses mentioned one specific episode with an escaped patient which led to the closing of the doors. She was a minister's wife who had escaped from the hospital for the second time. Because of her husband's community position, a group of attendants was sent to the home to bring her back. She had several children, and in order to return her, the attendants found it necessary to pry one of the children from her arms.

It was on the day of the escape, May 11, 1955, that the chief of service proceeded to lock the doors of the wards.*

---

* The superintendent states that the doors had to be closed at about this time to facilitate the refurbishing of the day room on that floor.

The staff criticized and severely resented the first program, because they had not been consulted about the decision to open the doors. One of the nurses commented that there had been no planning or working out of problems beforehand,** and two others mentioned that personnel were not given needed support and encouragement. An attendant said "there was no support from above" during this period, that it had been a very frustrating experience and a "headache" to all the personnel.

In summary, there seemed to be a marked rejection of the whole program by personnel working most closely with the patients on the wards. Perhaps this is why nurses and attendants, social workers, and occupational therapy workers remembered incorrectly that the doors had been opened "from a few days to a couple of weeks." The ward personnel's objections to the program can be placed in four categories: (a) threat to their personal security; (b) threat to their control of the ward situations; (c) dislike of having to call upon higher authority (the police) because of an expected increase in escapes; and (d) their feeling that patients felt insecure when the door was open.

PRELUDE TO THE SECOND EXPERIMENT

On November 26, 1956, the possibility of reopening the locked door was discussed among the staff during a Total Treatment Staff Meeting, a weekly session at this time open to all hospital personnel and moderated by the assistant superintendent. A member of the nursing personnel requested validation of the rumor that the open door policy was again being considered for the closed wards. Feelings of opposition were expressed by many, and most vociferously by the charge nurses who would be specifically affected by this policy. The degree of objection appeared to be related to the amount of contacts with patients—nurses and attendants being the most opposed. Specific fears were expressed concerning court cases, suicidal and homicidal patients.

** The superintendent's recollection was that there had been considerable discussion of this problem with numerous personnel for six months preceding the opening of the door.

The failure of the first experiment of unlocking the door was cited. The policy of the open door was felt to be a superficial display intended to maintain the hospital's reputation as a humane and pioneering institution.

Numerous thorny problems were raised. Who would be stationed at the door—a nurse, an attendant, a volunteer, a convalescent patient? How would visitors react upon encountering the more disturbed patients in the corridors of the hospital? What restrictions would be placed upon patients who needed more external control? It was decided that further discussion be postponed until the superintendent of the hospital could be present.

The following week the discussion was continued with the superintendent present. The recreational therapist expressed the opinion that discussion was unnecessary, fruitless, and only after the doors were opened would there be tangible problems to discuss. One of the Ward 4 male attendants could see no reason for opening the door in view of the "court cases who can then escape easily. . ." "Oftentimes they walk right past a nurse when there isn't an attendant available. . . . To leave the door wide open is asking for more trouble."

A nurse said that a change in attitude of the personnel would be necessary if the doors were to be opened. A number of times she had opened the door only to have it locked again by someone else. She said, "I don't think we are ready to open the doors because of the court cases. The way I look at it is that the subject should be dropped until the court cases can be screened. Of course, if we had a fenced-in outside prairie, then doors could be opened freely; but as I see it now, this would only create a nuisance."

The policy of opened doors in England was then described and the moderator emphasized that the success of the program lies in the fact that patients are properly oriented upon admission to the hospital and that high morale is created by delegating responsibility for making this program successful to the patients themselves.

A doctor said, "Ex-patients tell us that their days in the closed wards were most humiliating. The time spent behind locked doors greatly damaged their self-esteem. I have never heard anybody say it was something they needed in order to get well."

It was suggested that perhaps it might be a relief to have an authority make the final decision and assume responsibility. Whereupon the recreational therapist opined that by having a group study the problem, a more favorable tone would be created; and this, in itself, would favor keeping the door open.

The superintendent then stated, "A sound suggestion would be, if you are going to do something, let's do it and get it over with. Two weeks from today we will come up with a scheme as to how it will be done and we will do it. Would that be satisfactory?"

It was decided that the nursing supervisor head a committee to plan for opening the doors. The superintendent suggested that this be discussed in two weeks, "I want to be around to get the impact."

HOW PATIENT GOVERNMENT HANDLED THE CHALLENGE

During the December 4th Patient Government Meeting, the topic of opening the door was discussed. Approximately 20 patients were present, four of whom were active participants in the discussion. Two nurses and one physician were present but participated only when information was requested.

The President introduced the subject with a brief resume of the previous episode when the doors were opened, remarking that the plan had been carried out without mishap, yet it did not succeed for some unknown reason. He then informed the group that "the people downstairs" (management) would like to open the doors again and made reference to the need for patients to cooperate, especially the "rambunctious patients" on Ward 4. One patient expressed the opinion that the majority were ready for it, while a small percentage were not. It was agreed that there were enough personnel to supervise those patients who might be restricted to the wards.

The question was raised by a male patient as to whether or not the patients could be trusted. Comments to this included:

107

"It's worth a try."

"It was done previously for eight months without mishap."

"It is up to the doctor to decide when a patient is ready for an open door situation."

"It will decrease the annoyance of always waiting for a nurse to open the door."

Some patients felt that the hospital would appear less like a prison and that it would be a boost to morale.

Patients' views about opening Wards 4 and 5 were made known in a letter from Patient Government to the assistant superintendent on December 5, 1956. They agreed that there should be two attendants or nurses by the door, that it was "worth a try" and that a few patients would have to be restircted to the ward.

PROCEEDINGS OF THE "OPEN DOOR COMMITTEE"

On December 10, 1956, the "Open Door Committee" met with the superintendent to discuss plans for unlocking the door. He oriented the group with these opinions:

The locked door only adds to the already traumatic experience of admission to the hospital.

It is objectionable and irritating to the family and relatives who are forced to wait outside the locked door before they can visit the patient. A feeling of neglect is thus conveyed to them.

The locked door symbolizes the idea that mental patients are different and dangerous. We are not consistent in that we attempt to counteract this idea in our hospital by giving the patient increasing liberties and responsibility, yet we continue to lock the doors behind them.

It is an indignity for the patients to live behind a locked door and to be under the care of personnel who carry keys.

It is another evidence of the tendency to use coercion for "security" purposes.

The open door is the last step in the evolution away from the use of force for protection of the patients. Physical restraint was also once regarded as necessary for security reasons.

108

The locked door makes it more difficult to reintegrate the patient to his home. Our present policy is that at the time of admission to the hospital, arrangements are made for the patient's return to his home. This hopeful attitude is then destroyed when the patient is taken to a locked ward.

The superintendent concluded by saying that the hospital would gain recognition for this advance and would set an example for others to follow. He admitted a deeply personal interest in unlocked doors and said he was "envious" of other hospitals that had opened their doors successfully. He then discussed obsolete methods of dealing with institutionalized patients that had been common practice at this hospital some years back, such as stripping patients of clothes and shoes and removing from their person all articles which might possibly be used as weapons. The locked door was referred to as being in principle a similar restraint. "We must make a compromise," he said, "and do that which is best for the majority. The fact that there are a few for whom the locked door is good is not a valid reason for subjecting the rest to it."

The recreational therapist believed that the success of the program would depend upon placing a mature, confident, and capable person at the door. He suggested one particular male attendant whom he considered qualified. The superintendent suggested that volunteers be recruited from among ward personnel to remain at the door when opened. For the first two weeks it would be opened only in the afternoon for two to three hours. The need for a desk at the door was expressed by the recreational therapist so that the prestige of the person assigned to this task would be enhanced.

The nursing supervisor expressed interest in eventually eliminating the person stationed at the door, and inquired about privileges that would be allowed patients during the time the door was open. The superintendent advised that the decision should be made through discussion between the patients' doctors and the nurses, and suggested that a good deal of discretion be used in view of the "current tendency towards overuse of restrictions."

The nursing supervisor felt that word should be circulated that the door would be opened for only a short time each day, pointing out that the head nurses were not quite ready for the change.

The superintendent set the date for the following Monday. He advised the nursing supervisor to speak to the nurses concerning the granting of hospital and ground privileges to the patients even before the door was opened.

FINAL STAFF DISCUSSION PRIOR TO OPENING THE DOOR

At the December 10th Total Treatment Meeting the chairman presented the opportunity for further discussion on opening the wards which, he stated, would take place the following Monday. A report of the committee meeting with the hospital superintendent was given by a member of the nursing personnel, supplemented by one of the nursing students. The director of nurses suggested that a male attendant who had had experience with the open door at the time it was first attempted, and who had expressed interest in this program, would be a good candidate to monitor the door when opened.

The door was opened on December 17, 1956 and the nursing supervisor informed the group Staff Meeting that day of plans to get the new program under way.

> ". . . We will have to go along with it from day to day, and if certain patients that are restricted—we have lists—insist on going to O. T., they shall be permitted to go. Naturally, we shall try to inform the patient that his doctor does not wish him to go off the ward, and to keep it as impersonal as possible." She suggested that there be facilities available for the patients to sign in and out so there would be a record of their whereabouts. The hospital superintendent agreed to this plan.

> The recreational therapist raised a question concerning restrictions which would be imposed upon the patients by the resident doctors once the doors were open. The superintendent replied, "They have the authority to do anything they want, and they have to get used to taking responsibility. It is no problem."

110

THE RESPONSE TO THE OPEN DOOR

On December 17, 1956, the door was opened for a few hours in the morning. Gradually the time was increased until it was open both morning and afternoon except for meal times. A male attendant monitored the door for a while. He saw to it that as far as possible only those with privileges went out and that each person took the responsibility to sign in and out at the desk beside the door. The monitors were carefully selected for their knowledge of patients, tact and enthusiasm for the open door idea. At times other personnel or volunteers were stationed at the desk.

For the most part, patients adjusted easily to the new situation and were cooperative in signing in and out. Most of them seemed to like the idea and to enjoy the greater freedom. "It makes me feel like I am in my own home. I am not dependent on someone to take me around." A few seemed so preoccupied with their thoughts that they gave no outward signs of awareness of the open door. Attendance at O. T. increased 50 per cent.

Several patients not on privileges made attempts to leave the area, but the alert attendants quietly returned them to the day room. Testing behavior of this kind was more prominent during the first few weeks than later, and as the patients and attendants became more accustomed to their roles under the new conditions, monitoring the door became less a formal procedure than a casual function that could be carried on from afar. Soon desk-sitting by the door disappeared altogether. Keys, one of the most significant symbols of helplessness to patients, became inconspicuous and their absence was a welcome relief to all. On two occasions when the door *was* locked, the noise resulting from its unlocking seemed loud and annoying.

NOTES FROM STAFF DISCUSSIONS

During the January 14th staff meeting, the subject was again discussed.

The recreational therapist suggested that regardless of opinions expressed by the staff the doors would have been opened anyway, for this decision had already been reached before personnel were consulted. The assistant superintendent then asked the group whether or not there existed some resentment as to the manner in which the problem had been handled. A. social worker felt this to be the usual procedure for such decisions, something which one becomes accustomed to after "being around here for awhile." She added, "I think it is fine that they make it . . . I didn't mean that as a critical remark either . . ."

An interpretation was then offered by one of the residents: "The resentment is that you are made to feel as if you are a part of it, when actually the issue has already been decided. You might as well take the opportunity to air your feelings, but you know it doesn't make much difference."

A nursing instructor felt it to be "important to discuss administrative decisions" and commented upon the "possibility of undoing that which had already been decided." The chairman agreed and added: "One of the adjustments we have to make is that somebody else runs the hospital . . . somebody in an administrative position has the final decision . . . and this is hard for us rebels to learn. However, this certainly doesn't mean that if staff comes up with reasonable objections, the decision cannot be revoked. This has been done in the past. Practically nothing should be done in a sense of coercion . . ."

The question was then raised as to who would be held responsible for escapes. A member of the nursing personnel said that the superintendent stated that he would accept full responsibility. It was pointed out by the chairman that, legally, his was the final responsibility in fact.

During a staff conference approximately six weeks after the door was opened, the superintendent asked for comments. The nursing supervisor indicated that it had been quite successful and that there had been no major difficulty with patients. "In the beginning," she went on, "patients had to become oriented to this—some were on restrictions while others were not— and explanations were necessary. Now there are many who do not want to go to different areas of the hospital."

Another nurse voiced a need for more personnel, since the open door was a great temptation to patients who wished to escape. The superintendent stated that the recent escapes had been from other wards and that he was pleased with the outcome of the new policy. However, the nurse declared that there had been *attempts* from Wards 4 and 5. A nursing supervisor remarked that the general atmosphere of the ward appeared to be more pleasant and relaxed, but the first nurse did not agree.

The occupational therapist noted that there were more patients coming to the O. T. department and that these patients appeared to be more satisfied. "If they have forgotten something on the ward," she said, "they think nothing of going back for it . . . they seem very much at ease about the whole idea."

ESCAPES

In view of the feeling of some personnel that there would be a marked increase in escapes after the doors were opened, we compared the statistics for the period December 1956-May 1957 with the previous six months—December 1955-May 1956 when the door was closed. We find that between December 1956 and May 1957, two male and two female patients escaped. Contrasting this with a similar period a year before, one female and four males escaped. A retrospective comparison between these times revealed no significant change in numbers of escapes due to the open door situation.

We also compared the open door period with the escape record a year later, that is, December 1957-May 1958, and find that a year after the open door policy was instituted, nine patients escaped in the six months interval, five men and four women. We are unable to account for the subsequent increase in the number of escapes. The fact is that the number of escapes is not considered a serious problem in the hospital community, and no suggestions have come to us to close the doors because of escapes. It must be noted that some of the escapes were from areas like occupational therapy or physical therapy where the patients had been authorized to go. Relatively few escapes were directly from the ward through the open door.

Since much of staff concern was about expected high escape rate of *court cases,* we obtained data pertinent to this point. We found that three of the five escapes in the December 1955-May 1956 period were court cases; two of the four cases in December 1956-May 1957; and two of the nine cases from December 1957-May 1958 were court cases. Certainly there has been no major change in the escape record of court cases resulting from the open door policy.

A BRIEF "BEFORE AND AFTER" ATTITUDE SURVEY

To supplement the information obtained from analysis of staff conferences and from direct observation, systematic interviews were held with personnel before and after the door was opened. The aim was to determine changes of attitudes, if any, of those in direct contact with patients, and such non-directive questions were asked as: "How do you feel about the open door?" or "What is your attitude toward the open door?"

STAFF ATTITUDES BEFORE THE DOOR WAS OPENED

On December 11 and 13, 1956, a few days before the doors were opened on the acute wards, we had the opportunity to interview 24 personnel:

1. *(2) Psychiatrists and (8) Graduate Nurses.* Both psychiatrists considered that the closed door gave comfort, security, and protection to the patients from themselves and their impulses. One said, "This idea is for the administrative staff of the hospital . . . it would make an impression that they are progressive."

The eight graduate nurses had mixed feelings. Some felt the hospital was doing it for publicity. "It might get us written up in the Reader's Digest again," "It would look good on paper."

Lack of personnel for more individual attention to patients was a real concern shared by the nurses. They also wanted assurance that a member of the upper hierarchy would assume responsibility for mishaps resulting from this policy.

114

They felt that the new policy was simply replacing a key with a human door. "I would like to see the door open without having someone sitting at the door. Some of the other nurses think it is ridiculous to pay personnel to do something a door would do. They feel you should open it with no strings attached or else keep it closed. I wonder how successful this thing will be *if the nurses are against it*." In their opinion the administrators planning the change were not truly aware of ward problems. Nurses were most concerned about the very sick patients, escapees, and court cases. They felt that with an open door policy, patients would be more apt to escape, the public would react unfavorably, and personnel would be overworked.

One of the nurses felt that the major problem did not lie with ward personnel, for they could be handled through education from the senior staff, but originated among the doctors themselves and their attitudes toward patients having free run of the hospital. In her opinion, the first experiment failed because it was neither structured nor well planned. She remarked, "If my sister were very sick I would want more safety precautions for her than an open door." She felt that the closed door was an important part of therapy. Her opinion was shared by other members of the nursing staff who believed that in the event of an open door, another closed ward would be necessary to shelter the sicker patients.

2. *(8) Student Nurses.* The students considered the door to be a security measure for the patients' fears. In their opinion, the open door would require constant supervision by nursing personnel and might be the cause of more escapes. One commented, "They can get out of this place as it is without putting this idea into their heads, and I feel if they are ready for open doors, they can be transferred to the open wards . . . What is the reason for putting patients in the hospital if they can walk out?"

3. *(6) Attendants.* They had expressed mixed feelings. They wished to be flexible, doing what was ultimately best for the patients. Most, however, did not like the idea of opening the doors. They felt the patients were insecure, but their greatest objection was over lack of personnel to carry out the policy.

"People are in here because they are insecure, they need a closed door. If they needed an open door, they could stay at home." The attendants thought the open door policy would encourage escapees, especially court cases. They were concerned about not knowing the patients from other wards, thinking that this would complicate matters. One attendant stated, "We don't think much about it. We feel it is too much responsibility for us. A man would just walk out. That is the general opinion."

STAFF ATTITUDES AFTER THE DOOR WAS OPENED

From January to March 1957, after the doors had been opened, 10 members of personnel were interviewed:

1. *(4) Graduate Nurses.* For the most part, their attitudes did not change. "This does not concern me; I am not working on the affected ward," said one nurse. "I would be resentful because it would present a certain problem—more responsibility." "I don't think it is much different on Ward 5 now than it was before. I don't see more patients up in O. T. It creates anxiety in personnel because of added responsibilities. If I were working up there, I would be anxious, but there is no sense in losing sweat over it."

Another said, "If the door is supposed to be opened, it should be opened without anyone at the door. This is just for the papers so that it can be written down that the doors are opened." However, she admitted having less trouble than she had anticipated: "There are hardly any escapes . . . some patients had to be brought back from the corridor." In her opinion the open door entailed a disadvantage because some patients were now restricted to the back of the ward, not being allowed into the day room, whereas before they had access to the entire physical setup of the ward. There was also the necessity to keep a constant watch on patients with suicidal tendencies.

2. *(3) Student Nurses.* They affiliate at the hospital for a three month period. Those interviewed belong to a new group who arrived shortly after the open door policy was in effect. *These students felt the policy to be beneficial to patients.* In their opinion, although they had no direct experience with the

116

closed door regime, the open door neither presented special problems nor meant more work.

3. *(3) Attendants.* Great change was found in the attitudes of this group. Most were enthusiastic. "The patients feel more free and do not misuse this advantage. It is not a problem and not additional work." However, one still felt it required too many members of personnel to cover it. "Like this morning," he said, "four patients blew up at once. I had to take time to go and lock the door. This cut off people returning from O. T." He believed the new policy to be a good morale builder for the patients. "This is an admission ward and the patient does not feel closed in. The open door gives the patients contact with reality. They can distinguish between the real and unreal, for they know whether they are restricted or not. If patients are not restricted, they do not charge for the door all the time. There should be three attendants on duty; one in O. T., one at the door, and another in the lounge, because the one at the door has to stay there," he added. Another attendant remarked that if a patient "does try to escape, many times it is just to try it out and see what would happen. They usually return on their own accord."

A remarkable change was noted in the attitude of the attendant who when interviewed in December stated, "We don't think much about it, we feel it is too much responsibility for us, etc. . . ." She now said, "We were much against it before the doors were opened, but now we think it's working well. At first, we had difficulties with some patients, but now there is no trouble. We really don't have any problems."

THE SITUATION TWO YEARS LATER

In February 1959, approximately two years after the historic opening of "the door" from day room to outer corridor, we returned to study the situation and ascertain what changes, if any, had taken place. Since any new development in management of patients is accompanied by considerable feeling, controversy and tension, it becomes difficult to assess how much of the reaction is due to the change itself, as against the response of the social system to the change.

117

Two significant developments affect the comparison of open door observations made at the end of two years with those made shortly after opening. One is a major change in ward policy, and the other is decentralization of occupational therapy activities.

(1) Recently all six wards of the hospital were put essentially on a rotation plan for admission of patients. This means that the primary criterion for admission to a particular ward is availability of a bed; therefore, acute, chronic and convalescent patients are distributed through all the wards. In the past, Wards 4 and 5 had been designated for the acutely ill and as their condition improved they were transferred to open convalescent wards. Now the patient remains on his original ward, regardless of his clinical state or social adjustment.

(2) Quickly following this change in policy was the decision to decentralize O. T. activities, placing in each area a complete O. T. unit and worker.

The appearance of the day room connecting Wards 4 and 5 is largely unchanged. A small table (instead of a desk) is close by the door and on it is the clip board with checkout forms. Standing on the table is a restriction bulletin board with posted lists of three types of restrictions: (a) patients restricted to day room only; (b) those who may go to O. T. and Physical Therapy only, and (c) those who may go to all authorized places.

The open door, now a long accomplished fact, is largely taken for granted by personnel and patients. Patients are quite conscientious about signing in and out and the attendant on duty is inclined to help them follow through rather than "police" them. Occasionally a patient will inquire of the attendant whether he is restricted. A frequent problem is best stated in the oft-heard phrase, "You can't tell the patients from the staff." The result is that staff and relatives have on occasion been questioned by the attendant; and sometimes a resourceful patient, armed with a disguise of books and papers, has attempted to slip past the attendant by saying she was a social worker.

The door is regularly closed at bedtime, much as it would be in any household. Once in a while a male patient assigned to clean

118

the day room will close the ward doors leading to it to permit uninterrupted mopping. Attendants have had to close the door momentarily as a safeguard when trying to take care of a difficult patient in the day room. As soon as the problem is handled, however, the door is reopened.

The matter of escapes has been a concern to newer personnel, but gradually they have adopted the attitude of experienced employes who feel that as long as they have allowed the proper patients to leave the day room, they do not bear the responsibility of those who escape. Time after time, in their experience, escapees have returned to the hospital unharmed on their own accord or by police or relatives.

In summary, therefore, when the problem of the open door is seen from the better perspective of two elapsed years, and without former effects clouding our vision, it is possible to frame our present judgment as follows: *The open door is a fait accompli. It is accepted. It is good.*

DISCUSSION AND CONCLUSIONS

The great impetus towards opening the doors in mental hospitals can be traced to the English pioneers. Dingleton Hospital in Edinburgh (2) has been completely open since 1949; Warlingham Park (3) is now completely open; Mapperly Hospital (4) has been gradually opening its doors for many years, and since 1952, has been a completely open hospital. Nethern Hospital near London, has only two closed wards; these remain closed because of staff's conviction that some patients benefit from a closed environment.

In June 1956, Stern (5) of Warwick Hospital in Hatton, England, opened his last closed door in a hospital of over 1,380 patients. Now 28 wards have 100 open and unguarded doors.

While most of these experiments have taken years to accomplish, Mandelbrote (6) in 1958 reported changing the Coney Hill Hospital with 690 patients from a closed to a completely open institution in six months; and Snow (7) in New York has recently

119

reported achieving a 95 per cent open hospital from a completely closed situation in 15 months.

American psychiatrists visiting the English hospitals have been impressed with their results. The New York State hospital superintendents who went abroad to observe methods of care were greatly impressed (8-9). Wilmer (10) developed his "therapeutic community" based at least partly on inspiration from the English experiments. Koltes (11) apparently found the methods of patient care in England both stimulating and instructive. Cameron (12) has been operating the Allan Memorial Hospital as an open mental hospital for many years.

Although conditions are impressive in some vanguard hospitals, the situation in England is not altogether rosy. Maclay (13) has indicated that in a survey of 106 big mental hospitals with a total of 2,684 separate hospital units, two-thirds were unlocked and *one-third locked by day.* Some 23 hospitals had less than four locked ward units, and eight hospitals had no locked ward units.

In America, Felix (14), in 1958, reported interesting data from the architectural study of the American Psychiatric Association which surveyed roughly 95 per cent of all mental hospitals in the United States and Canada. Two or three hospitals reported all of their patients on open wards with freedom of movement, a few hospitals had no open wards and very few with privileges. Taking the United States as a whole, the overwhelming majority of hospitals are not open at all.

It would appear, therefore, that although much interest is expressed currently in the open hospital, a great many doors are still closed to mental patients. The open hospital idea has still to find practical reality in many institutions both here and abroad.

BRINGING ABOUT AND MAINTAINING NEW INSTITUTIONAL POLICY

Perhaps the most crucial factor in institutional change is the relation between administration and ward staff. There is abundant evidence that policy change can be successfully carried out when staff participate to some degree in the decision for change.

120

The reports abound in such statements as "staff must approve of all changes made;" (13) "staff must be stimulated and supported" (5). At least the following conditions must be met: (1) consistent support from above, from administration that is unwavering in its conviction that an open hospital is a therapeutic advance, and in its expectation that such can be achieved without serious mishap; (2) understanding of the fears and anxieties of staff; (3) development of instrumentalities for promoting expression of staff feeling and resolution of tensions; and (4) a broad base of mutual participation in the educational process of learning about problems of the open door and their solution.

Without free discussion and analysis jointly by administration and staff, it may be difficult for staff to appreciate that the balance between external and internal restraint is a fluid one, that many external restraints may be omitted or abolished under favorable conditions—to be replaced by internal controls which may be just as reliable, often more reliable than external ones (15-16). In discussing his observations in an American mental hospital, Charles Dickens expressed this concept very well. ". . . Moral influence alone . . . is found, even as a means of restraint, to say nothing of it as a means of cure, a 100 times more efficacious than all the strait-waistcoats, fetters and handcuffs, that ignorance, prejudice, and cruelty have manufactured since the creation of the world" (17). Moral influences include the subtle effect on patients of the physical and social environment especially the force of staff expectations and anticipations.

Staff problems are numerous: feelings of threat as to their personal safety or the safety of patients if the doors are open; fear of loss of authority if patients are allowed more freedom or are given a voice in the management of ward life; fear they will be singled out for blame if the patient has a mishap when he is away from the ward; or fear of an increasingly close relationship between the doctor and the patient. They are especially vocal regarding difficulties and stresses that may arise in the case of habitual absconders, suicidal cases, or senile brain-damaged subjects who may wander away and possibly meet with accidents on the highways. Where the hospital feels a great responsibility for court cases, and the law expects security provisions against escape, greater concern may be expressed (18).

All open hospitals have developed some instrumentality to alleviate tensions and anxieties of staff, as well as a medium for education. This usually involves diminishing the gap between nursing service and medical and administrative staff—a highly desirable goal under any circumstances. Group meetings that provide a forum for staff expressions, community meetings (10) or regular sessions with heads of all services arranged by the superintendent—all seem desirable. Often direct contact with administrative officers needs to be encouraged with an opportunity for both staff and patients to voice grievances. Although the specific instrumentality may vary the goals are generally the same—to help staff accept the open door policy, support it, and learn from it. Not infrequently, as in this experience, those staff members with the greatest direct responsibility for care of patients *on the ward* will be most opposed to the open door; this, then, may guide us as to where the most intensive work with staff is indicated.

Staff may be required to do intensive work with patients who find unusual difficulty in adapting to new freedoms. Intensive individual or group therapy may be required for those who habitually escape, or for deteriorated schizophrenic patients. This is especially recommended by Rees, MacMillan, Wilmer, and Cameron, and implies training of staff in individual and group dynamics as part of the preparation for the open ward. An active sociotherapeutic program is also recommended to involve the energies and interests of patients who might otherwise find the open door too threatening.

Wisebord *et al.*, (19) interviewed 55 of 86 female patients, mostly schizophrenic, as regards their attitude to the open door. Many expressed appreciation of greater liberty, increased self-esteem, sense of reliability, and less boredom. They apparently had fewer tensions, were given less to temper outbursts or brooding, and had better appetite and sleep habits. Scott (20) interviewed 35 chronic patients three weeks after the ward was

122

opened. The majority liked the change; however, about one-fourth wanted doors locked and some 12 per cent were indifferent. Patients may fear violence from other patients, or association with a disliked person. As one patient put it after the door was open, "Anyone can get in now."

It must be noted that after a lapse of time very few or none of the patients and staff desire to return to the situation of lesser freedom. Certainly new patients and new staff accept the arrangement as given and would be upset if they were suddenly asked to live under conditions of increased restraint. The indifferent, negative or rebellious attitudes of patient and staff are thus to be taken as the effects of accommodation to a specific cultural milieu and not necessarily part of disease, inherent negativism, or contentiousness.

Although a considerable improvement in staff-patient relationships appears necessary *before* the door can be opened, ideal staff-patient relationships cannot be achieved except *after* the door is open, for only the open door can undo staff embarrassment and conflict about being both jailer and healer at the same time.

Some consideration has been given to the relationships between outside community attitudes and the open door (21). Improving hospital-community relationships and educating the public to an understanding of mental illness and the mental hospital is a desirable end in itself—but to what extent is this a precondition to opening the door? Some administrators see public acceptance of the change as a necessary precursor, for the unsophisticated layman with his fantasies of madmen in the bedrooms, may be resistantly opposed to the idea. Others, especially Hunt, have said, "Before we can hope to make any serious change in public attitudes, we who work in the mental hospitals must bring about radical changes in our own institutions." The argument is that the fait accompli of the open door may be a powerful force towards revamping public attitudes. We suspect a great deal may depend upon the community in which the hospital is located, but that Hunt is right when he intimates that initiative and responsibility rest with hospital administrators to do the best they can for patients within their own institutions.

Lastly, we should emphasize that the open door is but one of many possible symbols of an institution advancing on the road towards greater patient freedom, more meaningful staff-patient relationships, and a better therapeutic climate. *An open door without an open mind is bound to be a failure.* An open door which is purely a fetish is meaningless. The open door should be part of a broad moving program to improve life for all; within this context it is one of the most graphic symbols of a growing therapeutic community.

ACKNOWLEDGMENT

The authors are grateful to Dr. Harry C. Solomon for criticisms and suggestions.

Many of the findings reported here stem from research conducted by the following nurses in partial fulfillment of requirements for Bachelor's Degree in Nursing at Boston University, 1957—Ruth Flynn, Genevieve Ginwala, Sylvia Orendenker, Cecelia Slavikova, Fay Siegal, Josephine Viens. We have attempted to preserve, as far as possible, the fresh observations and spirit of their original manuscript.

BIBLIOGRAPHY

1. Greenblatt, M., York, R. H., and Brown, E. L.: *From Custodial to Therapeutic Patient Care in Mental Hospitals.* New York, Russell Sage Foundation, 1955.

2. Bell, G. M.: A mental hospital with open doors. *Int. J. Soc. Psychiat.,* 1: 42, 1955-56.

3. Rees, T. P., and Glatt, M. M.: The organization of a mental hospital on the basis of group participation. *Int. J. Group Psychiat.,* 5: 157, 1955.

4. MacMillan, D.: Hospital-community relationships. In: *An Approach to the Prevention of Disability from Chronic Psychoses.* New York, Milbank Memorial Fund, 1958.

5. Stern, E. S.: Operation sesame. *Lancet,* 1: 577, 1957.

6. Mandelbrote, B.: An experiment in the rapid conversion of a closed mental hospital into an open door hospital. *Mental Hygiene, 42:* 3, 1958.

7. Snow, H. B.: The open door concept. *Mental Hospitals, 9:* 33, 1958.

8. Hunt, R. C.: Ingredients of a rehabilitation program. In: *An Approach to the Prevention of Disability from Chronic Psychoses.* New York, Milbank Memorial Fund, 1958.

9. O'Neill, F. J.: Laying the foundations for an open mental hospital. *Mental Hospitals, 9:* 10, 1958.

10. Wilmer, H. A.: Psychiatric therapeutic community in a naval hospital. *J.A.M.A., 166:* 1445, 1958.

11. Koltes, J. A.: Mental hospitals with open doors. *Am. J. Psychiat., 113:* 250, 1956.

12. Cameron, D. D.: The open hospital. *Mental Hospitals, 5:* 3, 1954.

13. Maclay, W. S.: *Experiments in Mental Hospital Organization.* (First Canadian Mental Hospital Institute Academic Lecture.) Ottawa, Mental Health Division, Dept. of National Health and Welfare, 1958.

14. Felix, R. H.: Legal and administrative implication of rehabilitation. In: *An Approach to the Prevention of Disability from Chronic Psychoses.* New York, Milbank Memorial Fund, 1958.

15. The unlocked door. *Lancet, 2:* 953, 1954.

16. Hurst, L. C.: The unlocking of wards in mental hospitals. *Am. J. Psychiat., 114:* 306, 1957.

17. Dickens, C.: *American Notes for General Circulation.* Third Edition. London, Chapman and Hall, 1842.

18. Garber, R. S.: Legal implications of the open hospital. *Mental Hospitals, 9:* 24, 1958.

19. Wisebord, N., Denber, H. C. B., Charatan, F. B., and Travis, J. H.: Patient reactions to the "open door." *Am. J. Psychiat., 115:* 518, 1958.

20. Scott, D.: Chronic mental patients' reaction to opening their ward. *Am. J. Psychiat., 113:* 366, 1956.

21. Royal Medico-Psychol. Assoc. Annual Meeting: Open doors in mental hospitals. *Int. J. Soc. Psychiat., 2:* 152, 1956.

125

DISCUSSION OF DR. GREENBLATT'S PAPER

DR. LEIGH M. ROBERTS:—

As Dr. Greenblatt has pointed out in his presentation, the open door may become a treatment fetish. In principle the retention of the rights of self-control, self-discipline and freedom by the patients in a hospital is desirable. This is true insofar as the patient is able to accept the responsibility for these rights in such a way as to avoid serious detriment to himself and others. When these must be restricted due to the illness, it would be best to use the interpersonal approach. The efficacy of this method in a well staffed and motivated state hospital is pointed out in the previous description of opening a locked door.

Caution must be exerted in avoiding usage of the open door as an isolated goal. It should be recognized that many of the values of an open door policy are more dependent on staff attitudes than on the act of opening the door. Attitudinally there may occur closed minds with an open door and open minds with a closed door. The need to train ward staff and work through their problems relative to the anticipated opening of the door as a necessary preparatory step is well documented.

The meaning of the door to individual patients in its closed or open state reflects the psychological state of the patient. Many patients request restriction imposed by others on their freedom of movement and activity at times when they feel unable to accept these responsibilities which they previously assumed. The restraint of chemotherapy, the support of interpersonal relationships and physical controls such as a locked door may all have a significant place in the therapy of individual patients in varied hospital settings.

It is doubtful if an open door is an *essential* component of *all* therapeutic communities as has been stated by some. The development of a series of vital healthy interpersonal relationships integrated as a community is more of the essence as members strive to assist each individual to most fully develop and utilize his interpersonal and intrapersonal potentialities.

126

DISCUSSION OF DR. GREENBLATT'S PAPER

Dr. Alexander Gralnick:—

There are several questions to keep in mind relative to the attempts mentioned to establish in the therapeutic community a situation similar to that which exists outside. First, it was in relative freedom outside that patients became sick. It was there that they decompensated. If we set up exactly the same type of freedom within our hospitals, how are we going to explain the improvements? Obviously something else is going on.

When Dr. Greenblatt speaks of the open door with a guard by it, this is pseudo-freedom. When Dr. Denber speaks of five dollars per month as compensation for a patient, this hardly resembles reality.

Yet, I believe Dr. Greenblatt has something when he says there can be no open door without an open mind. However, an "open mind" may call for a closed door for certain patients. To force such patients into an open ward may be denying them the freedom they require.

When Dr. Greenblatt describes the negotiations which went on between the patients and himself as an authority figure, he is telling us about realistic and rational behavior. Out of this negotiation came the decision to open the ward's door. It was this rational behavior between them which was therapeutic, not merely opening the door.

I think we are still searching for something in our discussions about the therapeutic community which we have as yet not found. I believe that being realistic is of considerable importance. The fact is that as doctors we are in a position of authority relative to the patient, and we have to exert it. The schizophrenic patient particularly has problems with authority. We cannot help him work them out by shirking our position. If we do, we may merely relieve pressure on him and some of his symptoms may disappear. The therapeutic community, however, should aim for more than a symptomatic change. We should want the reconstructive

127

change that can only come from working out the patient's emotional problems.

Essentially, we are trying to determine what are rational or "therapeutic" interpersonal relationships between patients and staff. These will and must differ in different hospitals, depending on the nature of its patients, its staff's approach to treatment, its physical plant, and a host of other factors. The determination of what is "realistic" will remain most difficult to judge.

DISCUSSION OF DR. GREENBLATT'S PAPER

Dr. Herman C. B. Denber:—

Many patients on the research ward have had long hospitalizations ranging up to 30 years. Reality for them, as implied by Dr. Gralnick, has lost all significance. A major aim of the therapeutic community project was their resocialization—a task literally herculean, for it involved reliving what had been forgotten. The idea of work had disappeared and money held no value; besides, it was not needed on the ward. For this reason, status was assigned to various positions by a symbolic monetary remuneration. Surprisingly enough, I have seen chronic patients making any small sum in our workshop approach a nurse and joyfully announce the fact.

GROUP MEETINGS
IN A THERAPEUTIC COMMUNITY

Leigh M. Roberts, M.D.

Emotional illness may be viewed as both an intrapersonal and an interpersonal phenomenon. The psychiatrist frequently thinks to a major extent of psychodynamics as intrapersonal and treatment measures are directed in accordance with these concepts. With the additional view of emotional illness as an interpersonal occurrence we are best prepared to center our treatment approaches on the milieu with maximum utilization of the hospital climate as a therapeutic community. The consideration of the hospital and individual hospital ward as a therapeutic community is difficult in terms of semantics. As pointed out by Wilmer (1), we are often speaking of quite different things as we use the term therapeutic community, but efforts at defining each of our hospital communities is a step toward common understanding.

The community described in this paper is Mendota State Hospital, one of two state mental hospitals in Wisconsin operated by the State Department of Public Welfare. Established in 1860, it is a 939 bed institution serving multiple functions though it is primarily for the treatment of acute mentally ill patients. It serves also for treatment of alcoholics and drug addicts, evaluation of court referred cases for mental and physical observation, long term treatment of the chronically disturbed mentally ill, and training of persons working in psychiatry and multiple allied fields.

The admissions during the last fiscal year consisted of 967 men and 563 women. The mean patient stay of three and five-tenths months in 1956 represents the last available figure. During the past fiscal year 796 patients were committed to the hospital through courts and 734 were voluntary patients. There were 801 men and 485 women who left the hospital during that year. The hospital population is mixed as to age, sex, race, religion, economic and social status, educational and occupational backgrounds. One unique feature of the Wisconsin hospital system is the use of multiple county hospitals for care of the more chronically ill keeping the larger state hospitals as more intensive treatment centers.

The usual disciplines are represented on the hospital staff with training programs for medical students, psychiatric residents,

131

student nurses, psychologists, social workers, occupational therapists, recreational therapists and chaplains as well as continuous in-service staff training programs. The treatment program includes electroconvulsive therapy and coma and subcoma insulin. The tranquilizing drugs are given to about one-half of patients. There is a moderate use of orthodox group therapy and limited use of individual psychotherapy.

The ratio of about 50 patients per physician provides limited psychiatric services to the majority of patients. The treatment program is implemented by extensive use of occupational, recreational and industrial therapy programs as well as vocational rehabilitation. These approaches on most of the hospital wards are coordinated with group meetings in an effort to derive maximal benefit from the milieu as a therapeutic agent.

It is important to recognize that a therapeutic atmosphere is one major treatment effort and not the panacea to mental illness. It can be used to provide the basic framework for other therapies which earlier have been found useful in treating patients. These other therapies are used as indicated on an individualized basis within the structure of a continuously functioning milieu. Our approach has not been extreme, but a modification of earlier practices. We have not banned somatic therapy, opened all wards, let patients decide all matters affecting themselves nor made all communications open to group scrutiny without maintaining confidentiality in the doctor-patient relationship. Some steps have been made in these directions with reduction in somatic therapy, development of patient government, opening some wards, and reduction of restraint as well as increasing ground privileges. Patients are permitted greater control over their possessions. There are increased opportunities for patient activity, and better avenues of communication have been established as part of the therapeutic community program.

A therapeutic community does not arise from mere good intent nor does it happen to develop by chance. It is a carefully structured, motivated and nourished form of treatment requiring continuous hard work on the part of the hospital team. In imple-

132

menting it there are a succession of steps which work with varying degrees of effectiveness in different settings. One major area has been establishing better channels of communication throughout all levels of the hospital but with particular emphasis on the individual wards.

Each hospital ward has its own distinctive and unique atmosphere. In many regressed wards a chronic schizophrenic reaction with withdrawal and regression constitutes an adequate adjustment. The unspoken prevailing attitude of patients on such a ward appears to be "You get along best here by never saying anything." Such attitudes are conducive to perpetuation of mental illness. Communication disruptions are to some extent causative in mental illness. Patients' perceptions usually reflect both realistic and distorted views of the ways staff persons react to them. The patient fears but often anticipates displeasure and negative responses from others. The greater the failure in communication in that type of environment, the stronger is the isolation of individual patients with appearance of more signs of autistic thinking and regressed behavior.

Avenues for re-establishment of communication must be found in order to have effective therapy. In addition to individual and group psychotherapy, which require many highly trained professional persons to reach relatively small numbers of patients, larger group and milieu therapy methods are particularly adaptable to a state hospital which has limited numbers of professionally trained staff.

One of the kinds of group meetings in our hospital might be labeled ward meetings. They are modifications of those used by Wilmer (2) and Jones (3). The ward patients, varying in number from 25 on continued treatment units to about 50 on admission units, and the ward staff meet as a group. Throughout this paper the terms staff and personnel are used synonymously. The staff includes physicians, nurses, aides, psychologists, social workers and other persons who work on that particular ward. All members are strongly urged to attend, and group pressure is used as a means of encouraging attendance.

133

The leadership of a meeting centers on one or two persons. The leader is usually either a physician, psychologist or social worker who is intimately acquainted with the patients and staff members. A co-leader role on some wards is filled by one of the nurses or aides. There are individual variations on the different wards but the most common pattern is the one cited here. On most wards the meetings take place 45 minutes daily on five days each week. The seating arrangement is casual and self-determined by the individuals though efforts are made by the leader to keep members fairly close together to facilitate communication. The meeting is opened by the leader with any person free to discuss a topic of their choice after acknowledgement.

Throughout the discussion comments on similar or dissimilar veins are presented by many patients and personnel. Specific psychological problems are not introduced by the leader except as they are seen within the meeting. There are many variations in the manner of conducting the meeting by different individuals with the degree of permissiveness, authoritarianism, verbal activity or passivity, emphasis on psychological problems or ward activities reflecting their personality. At times psychodramas are given, and in some situations movies have been shown followed by a group discussion of the predominate theme. On some wards anonymous suggestions or ideas may be submitted by use of a suggestion box, while on other wards such anonymity is discouraged.

In any group meeting a large number of variables are present contributing to the group process. The arrangement of chairs in a circle, rectangle or irregular configuration, the distance of individual members from each other and from the leader, the locations of the leaders within the group, the location of specific "talkative" or hyperactive members and the presence or absence of furniture all appear to have an influence on the group discussion. The 52 bed ward where the study cited took place was primarily that of disturbed schizophrenic relatively newly admitted patients on active treatment.

There are frequent shifts of patients with admissions, moves to convalescent wards or discharges resulting in an average population change of about two persons daily. The group composition and the frequent patient movement constitute major determinants of the type of interactive group process. The depletion of the group by removal of the patients who are best able to engage in more integrated group interaction and their replacement by those much less able to communicate is reflected continuously within the group. The presence of from 40 to 65 persons in the ward meetings and the problems inherent in developing free communication among a majority of the group due to its size as well as the degree of illness in its members led to substitution of smaller groups on many wards a portion of the time. Each type of group meeting was held several times each week.

On the ward previously cited, the patient and staff membership is divided into fifths for the creation of the smaller groups. This results in a group size of from eight to 13 with about three-fourths of the group being patients and the remainder personnel. Members remain with the same group during their stay on the ward. We have been impressed with the greater ease of communication in the smaller group. This ability to communicate develops despite marked group heterogeneity and the severity of illness in the patient members. It is as if the smaller group is a learning experience in group process for both patients and staff members which can be transferred in part to a larger group.

Leadership in the small groups rests with the doctors, psychologists and social workers who are actively working on the particular ward, with the nursing and aide staff functioning as co-therapists. Membership changes in the small groups occur at a rate of about three per group weekly, effecting at times marked shifts in the nature of the group and its ability for effective interaction. Despite this, much of the group process is similar to group therapy at various stages of development.

The key to successful group interaction rests on the skill, training and sensitivity of the group leader as he attempts to focus on group interaction while also providing maximum therapeutic help

135

to individuals. The best leaders are not necessarily those who have the most professional status on the ward, and efforts are made to utilize others with lower status who possess qualities of leadership.

The purposes of the various group meetings are in many ways identical with the aims of milieu therapy. The meetings are a concentrated condensed specific sample of the interactive process which occurs in a less highly organized manner the remainder of the time. The atmosphere of the ward is clearly reflected in the meeting and conversely the climate of the meeting helps to determine the atmosphere of the ward.

The ward meeting is a community in action and constitutes a fairly stable social situation in which the destructive disintegrative actions of specific individuals do not significantly alter the social structure. In this atmosphere individuals find acceptance and personal security lessening their need to react in socially unacceptable ways. The attitudes and actions of the staff are important in exemplifying ways of accepting such behavior. Some of the goals might be listed as enhancement of patient-patient, patient-staff and staff-staff communications and relationships, greater patient participation in planning their own program and more actively guiding their own treatment on the ward, providing more opportunities for reality testing in individual and group relationships, staff development through increased training and creation of a ward treatment team.

Some of the effort is directed toward creation of a closely integrated community group by enhancing interpersonal relationships. Out of this arises a sense of personal responsibility, retention of individuality within the group, feelings of being trustworthy, self-respect and a sense of personal identity which is also shared by staff members. The whole group increasingly becomes cohesive as a community, although this fluctuates markedly as the constituency alters. Group controls are used to diminish acting out by individual members while encouraging more desirable and acceptable behavioral responses.

136

The repetitive negative social interaction patterns of individuals are frequently interrupted when they as persons are accepted by the group. Negative behavior is then replaced by purposeful activity and positive social interaction. The opportunity is afforded for reality testing, catharsis and resolution of individual and group problems. More effective patterns of behavior are demonstrated to the maladapting patient which may then be learned. Much of the interchange is more on an emotional than an insight basis, though this varies according to group membership. Nonetheless, many leaders place emphasis on introspective evaluation of individual attitudes and emotions for both patient and staff members. The group sessions offer a constant training period for staff members as well as a therapeutic climate for patients.

Varied types of psychopathological symptomatology may appear as partial reflections of the environment. It is a common experience to see a group of schizophrenic patients react quite differently as they move to a new environment. The reactions of others within the environment help determine the responses of even very psychotic persons, and the behavior of staff members tends to reinforce or diminish the appearance of specific types of behavior; aggressive behavior by a patient may follow threatening or challenging attitudes by staff members. Pointing out these kinds of reaction patterns is one of the functions of the meetings.

A major problem in the evaluation of a therapeutic community lies in the determination of what is "therapeutic." The characteristics of therapeutic factors are difficult to measure with any exactitude when considering the many variables. In order to make the results of such research very meaningful, it seems necessary to have matched control groups, including patients and staff, similar in all areas but for the milieu therapy being assessed. By clinical impression, milieu approaches were quite effective. But there is obviously much individual distortion in such evaluations by staff members with their emotional investment in the results. The subjective evaluations of patients in these areas are subject to similar distortion. Lacking a matched control group to evaluate the effectiveness of the milieu approach, our study investigated the problems from a different direction.

An earlier study by McDermid (4) on one of the hospital admission wards explored the dynamics of the ward meetings. Verbal participation, affect, topic of discussion and the Anxiety-Repression scale (5) were measures used in that research pilot study. Statistically significant relationships were demonstrated between the following variables: 1) a direct relationship between patient and staff preferences for certain meetings, 2) a direct relationship between the leader and patient preferences for certain meetings, 3) a direct relationship between patient preference for a meeting and that patient's verbal participation, 4) an inverse relationship between patient participation and that patient's level of anxiety and 5) an inverse relationship between patient preference for a meeting and the total number of staff responses in that meeting. Meetings were most preferred when the topics of discussion were psychological matters, home, family and ward problems in that descending order. It was concluded that a complex interplay of dynamic factors operated in the meetings for which further research efforts were indicated using a matched control group.

Evaluation of staff attitudes were attempted recently by a questionnaire focused on milieu meetings. It consisted of 55 items ranging from open ended to forced choice items and some requests for comments in an effort to approach each aspect of the meeting in different ways. The 54 anonymous respondents included 12 nurses, 19 aides and 23 professional persons (physicans, psychologists and social workers). All were working on four admission wards holding similar ward meetings. Three wards were holding small group meetings in addition.

It was clear from the responses that marked variation was present in the reactions of individuals to every phase of the meetings without unanimity on any question. Patterns were evident reflecting group sentiment and they largely confirmed earlier impressions of staff attitudes. These patterns were part of the staff group culture, though each member retains his individuality in areas which attitudinally were not in conformity with the over-all cultural pattern. The statistical significance of multiple hypotheses based on these responses was measured by the chi square test. Caution must be exercised in interpreting the data in terms of the relatively small number of individuals involved despite the statistical significance of the data. Similarly, the defects involved in use of a questionnaire to obtain data call for further consideration of the results obtained as valid only insofar as that instrument provides reliable information.

The preferred items of discussion in a "good" meeting, as considered by staff members, were self-attitudes, attitudes toward emotional illness, ward problems and interpersonal problems between patients or patients and staff. Ward rules, "very personal" problems which were not further defined and problems between patients and staff members were more frequntly listed as topics in a "poor" meeting. Nurses were more concerned about ward rules, aides less concerned about patient-staff relationships and other staff members more concerned about patient-patient problems as meeting topics.

The major element in group process was good participation and free communication by both patients and staff members. Lesser emphasis was placed on developing a cohesive group, an understanding of patients as revealed in the meeting, catharsis by patients and resolution of the problems presented. Elements in a poor meeting contributing to the negative connotation consisted of dominance by a single patient, poor participation and communication, presence of marked hostility and the leader's failure to actively direct the meeting.

Lesser consideration was given to negative staff attitudes and the leader's failure to answer questions directed to him. The nurses were less concerned about good communication than other personnel and less tolerant of marked patient hostility. The nurses and aides were less concerned about negative staff attitudes than other personnel in evaluating the constituents of a poor meeting. The topics of religion and politics were listed by some as undesirable and no one described them as topics in a good meeting.

A good leader was described as one who answered questions, obtained maximum group participation and emotional involvement and focused on emotions rather than discussion content. Less frequent qualities were maintenance of order, active participation, attention to a group focus and non-directive guidance. The majority felt that both patients and personnel should be asked to volunteer comments in preference to either relying solely on those who request to speak or by calling on non-volunteers from either group.

A poor leader was one who failed to answer direct questions from the group, was overly passive, relatively non-verbal and failed to understand the staff views and emotions. To a lesser extent, he may fail to understand patients or be overly active verbally to the point of inhibiting communication. The view of the poor leader failing to answer direct questions was held more frequently by nurses and aides than by other staff members.

The presence of visitors in meetings was a contentious issue with about one-half of the personnel on each side of the question. This conflict has been reflected in strong statements that visitors may express ideas based on minimal knowledge derogatory to the staff members. Others felt equally strong that visitors were not contributory to patient discomfort if they participated in the meeting, and that their ideas were welcomed as a valued addition to any discussion.

The preferred frequency of ward meetings was from three to five times per week and for smaller group meetings twice weekly by a large majority of the staff. The areas where change was desired centered on greater participation of all members of the group and greater verbal activity of the leader, including direct answers being given to patients. Responses were about equally divided on the belief that the meetings were of greatest benefit to either the total ward or to the patient segment of the ward with a few persons believing it helped the staff more than the aforementioned groups. It was believed that the meetings were worth the time spent on them ($P = .01$). The meetings were also viewed

as making the ward a more therapeutic place for patients to resolve their emotional problems ($P = .01$).

The time expended on meetings was a source of conflict to
many staff members. This kind of conflict appeared to basically
approach the individual's self-concept as it applied to his work.
Each person endeavors to fulfill his job as he perceives it and the
kind of transition requested of the ward employee in changing a
ward from a custodial to a therapeutic atmosphere is a difficult
one. The acceptance of meetings which mobilize anxiety and
conflicts in patients or precipitate acting-out behavior poses difficulties for some older employees who have worked for years in a
regressive non-stimulating ward atmosphere. The frequent alterations in ward rules following patient suggestion, the reduction of
status in the hierarchy and lessening of rigid authoritarian controls was hard for nurses whose personality patterns were of an
authoritarian type.

Nurses and aides who perceived their roles in terms of administration, housekeeping, traditional nursing procedures or custodial
care of patients found it difficult to spend daily periods of time in
group centered activity, such as the ward meetings, where definitive structuring of their role could not be as readily seen or appreciated as was their previous role. Difference of opinion between
nursing supervisors and ward leaders may lead to divergent pressures on employees. Young psychiatrists trained and interested in
the individual psychotherapeutic approach found it difficult to
accept milieu treatment as an equally valuable experience for the
patients and themselves. However, these conflicts were sufficiently
resolved for most to permit their acceptance and help in the
milieu program.

Many staff members have reservations about moving too far
towards patient self-direction. These views appeared to permeate
a significant segment of all groups sampled including those with
a variety of previous training experiences. It was easier for many
of the personnel to make repeated small progressive moves than
to make greater ones at less frequent intervals. Though many
changes met with marked resistance they could gradually be ac-

cepted and incorporated into ward policy and procedure with comfort.

The small groups were preferred by most staff members over the larger ward meetings (P = .01) largely on the basis of feeling more at ease and having greater ease in verbally participating. Most staff members found it easier to comment in group therapy than in the ward meetings (P = .01). Preference was expressed for the leadership in both meetings to remain with a staff member who worked on the ward as contrasted with one who was not as familiar with the patients and personnel (P = .01).

One of the major areas of this study centered on problems in communicating at the ward meeting. The leaders have expressed the view consistently that other staff members are not as verbally expressive as is desirable. Many individual staff members are able to function well in this area but others may remain silent unless a specific topic pertaining to them is introduced by others. The aides are not accustomed to speaking before a group and patterns of this type are not readily altered, despite encouragement by the leader and efforts to make them comfortable in doing so. The easiest problems for staff members to discuss are ward rules and difficulties in the relationship between a staff member and a patient.

The major expressed reasons for difficulty in communication were failure to understand the function of the meetings, failure to have the individual role of the nurse or aide well-defined, feeling ill-at-ease in the meeting, feeling the negative responses of the patients directed at the staff and discomfort over marked hostility by patients in the meeting. Less frequently mentioned were lack of emotional support from other staff members, minimal participation by others, difficulty in formulating and verbalizing ideas for presentation and personal feelings of insecurity. Some expressed the opinion that patients should do most of the discussing and others felt unable to answer the queries directed at them by patients, thus increasing the staff member's feelings of inadequacy.

The staff were asked for their preference of leadership by the various professional groups. The expressed preference appeared

142

to vary in direct proportion to the hierarchical status of that group on the ward. The ratings in descending order were physician, psychologist, social worker, nurse and aide. This preference order was true for all groups sampled without exception. Efforts at encouraging maximum participation have included joint leadership by nurses and aides with the other categories of leaders resulting in some increase in overall staff verbal participation.

The personnel were divided by wards with a sub-group from each of four admission wards. The views of the staff on three of the wards were very similar throughout despite individual ward variations in their milieu program. On the fourth ward the meetings were not felt to be worth the time spent as assessed by the majority of the personnel and a plurality felt the meetings made the ward a harder place to work. The majority of that staff believed ward meetings should be held once weekly with ward rules and ward problems as the topics but not bringing up "very personal" problems.

The majority on that ward also stated they would discontinue the ward meetings entirely if it were up to them. These views were quite at variance with those on the other wards though active resistance to changing traditional nurse-aide roles was experienced as each ward developed this kind of program. The ward with these negative attitudes had most recently evolved their meetings.

Implementation of a therapeutic community means abandonment of traditional methods of maintaining a pleasant quiet ward. A premium is placed on socialization of patients with each other and with the staff. The opportunities for greater expression of all types of emotional responses including hostility and acting out is increased. This places great demands on the skill and personal abilities of aides and nurses. Housekeeping chores are de-emphasized as a major activity of the aides. The overt hostility level on the ward at times is high. In the midst of this the ward personnel have strong needs for training, guidance and emotional support. At times the latter needs are so strong that they are difficult to meet in face of equal demands by patients.

Throughout the survey of personnel attitudes the need to have the leader answer questions directly in order to bring them to a resolution was expressed. This was particularly true of aides and nurses to whom the questions would later be referred if left unresolved. It is difficult for many members to accept the concept of unresolved issues carried on to later discussions. This same difficulty is frequently expressed by patients who seek authoritative answers to many issues which they subsequently resolve by individual or group decision.

One of the clearest demonstrations of the interactive process between individuals at all status levels is seen in the ward meetings. Unresolved intra-staff conflict or hostility is readily perceived by patients and may be magnified or reflected in patient acting-out behavior. Similarly, resolution of these problems is seen in a return of tranquility to the ward. Periods of prolonged disturbed behavior by a group of patients usually reflect the inability of the personnel to function cohesively in analyzing and arriving at therapeutic handling of patient problems. Patients are rarely disturbed and less frequently create significant problems when the personnel have sufficiently resolved their own problems and function well as members in the community.

Efforts are continuously made to keep the ward communities as similar to the non-hospital community as possible. The greater the differences in the two environments the greater are the adjustment problems on leaving the hospital. Making an adjustment to a hospital ward grossly dissimilar to the non-hospital environment may lead to a successfully managed hospital stay but need not be conducive to resolving interpersonal difficulties out of the hospital.

Some of the efforts to maintain a setting similar to the extrahospital community are directed towards continuous patient activity. This planning is one of the items considered in ward meetings with the initiative coming preferably from patients. Their committees, with or without ward personnel as members, plan for work and recreational activity. The extent to which these groups are successful is as dependent on the attitudes of staff members as it is upon the patients. They function with varying degrees of effectiveness on different wards depending on the staffs and kinds of patients.

The effectiveness of a therapeutic community approach depends largely on personnel. It is difficult to effect its adoption and maintenance without active administrative support. Below the administrative echelon enthusiastic leadership must be provided by the ward physicians. In some instances where this quality was lacking the overall program was less well developed and proved only partially successful.

The ward charge nurse's leadership of her staff is another major factor. They interact most directly with patients and the success of the community rests on this ability to develop a therapeutic climate. Formal as well as continuous informal training and discussion periods are essential in developing their ability to meet the needs of this task.

One major function of meetings has been staff development. A great effort has been extended in this direction with the goal of helping to develop individual therapeutic attitudes. In an institution with fair stability in its aide staff (13 per cent turnover in those positions last year), there are many persons who have worked for years in the hospital when custodial management exceeded therapeutic expectations.

Part of this training is conducted in daily staff meetings for a period of 30 minutes following the ward or group therapy meetings. They are attended by all ward staff members. The multiple foci in this meeting range from social to educational. Development of group cohesion, discussion of the preceding ward meeting with the patients, the current ward problems, intra-staff conflicts, changes in ward policy, discussion of the dynamics or therapeutic approach to the problems presented by a specific patient and a variety of other issues may be covered in an informal discussion by all ward staff members.

Study of the ward and other group meetings in the therapeutic community point out the necessity for further research in this area. Many questions are raised relative to the effectiveness of this program which are best answered by comparison with a control group. Continued study of the dynamics within the community, including careful descriptions of the observations of non-involved persons, may indicate the direction for further changes which will prove therapeutic.

SUMMARY

The implementation of a ward therapeutic community by means of group meetings is presented. The functions of the ward meetings are multiple and in many ways include most of the functions of a therapeutic community. They constitute a means of staff development and provide a demonstration of the interactive process on the ward. The evaluation of these meetings by staff members has led to an analysis of what constitutes positive and negative meetings in terms of leadership, emotion and content. These evaluations have not been correlated with "therapeutic" benefit in these studies for which further research is indicated.

BIBLIOGRAPHY

1. Wilmer, H. A.:   Toward a definition of the therapeutic community. *Am. J. Psychiat., 114:* 824, 1958.

2. Wilmer, H. A.:   A psychiatric service as a therapeutic community. *U. S. Armed Forces Med. J., 7:* 640, 1956.

3. Jones, M. S.:   The therapeutic community.   New York, Basic Books, 1953.

4. McDermid, C. D.:   *Pilot Study: The Therapeutic Community.* Unpublished, 1957.

5. Welsch, G. S., and Dahlstrom, W. G.:   *Basic Readings on the MMPI in Psychology and Medicine.*   Minneapolis, University of Minnesota Press, 1957.

DISCUSSION OF DR. ROBERTS' PAPER

DR. MAX RINKEL:—

I enjoyed Dr. Roberts' paper very much, and I wish to congratulate him for his concise yet comprehensive presentation. When we talk about "Group Psychotherapy" we think of an innovation inaugurated by we psychiatrists and springing from the desire to give psychotherapy to as many patients as possible by the extremely limited number of psychiatrists available in any major mental hospital. However, the idea of organized group psychotherapy was conceived and put into action by a medical man long before its current use in psychiatric hospitals.

As early as 1905, Dr. Joseph H. Pratt, late Professor of Clinical Medicine at Tufts College Medical School, conducted the first medical group therapy for tubercular patients. On April 11, 1930, he started group psychotherapy as a Thursday morning class in the medical clinic of the Boston Dispensary. This developed when a study of 2,000 consecutive cases in the Boston Dispensary Out-Patient Department revealed that 30 per cent of these patients had medical complaints with no apparent organic causation. As in our state hospitals, there were not enough therapists available to give individual psychotherapy to the many patients with psychosomatic complaints. Dr. Pratt, therefore, inaugurated what then was called the "Thought Control Class" (a name suggested by one of the first patients), and is now known under the name of "Classes In Applied Psychology." More than 7,000 patients have been treated there.

These classes are based on eight psychotherapeutic principles, as Johnson stated them: (1) The common ground: The patients derive assurance from the fact that other people have similar complaints. (2) Public relation: Group therapy provides the releasing opportunity to discuss openly with others disturbing problems; freedom to express anxieties is a catharsis which leads to healthier attitudes towards these anxieties. (3) Personal attention: Utmost personal attention is given to each patient by roll call, attendance score, individual reports, discussion of typical

147

problems, friendly greeting, praise for progress and concern for lack of it. (4) Reporting progress: Members report their progress which gives added motivation for recovery. (5) Relaxation: Instructions are given on how to relax muscles from head to toe, using the Jacobson method of progressive relaxation; mental exercises are then followed and directed to gain repose and emotional serenity. (6) Emotional re-education: This teaches the patient what he can do for himself. (7) Acting on new insights: The patient is asked to perform the simple muscle relaxing exercises at regular intervals during the week; as the patient leaves the first class with something definite to work on, he decides, "This I can do." (8) Working perspective: To act upon lessons learned leads to a sense of freedom to do more easily what needs to be done; distorted prejudices, fears and hostilities yield to a working perspective that leads to healthier living.

As the psychotherapeutic principles indicate, the technique in conducting the class consists essentially of two basic procedures: Manipulation of the patient, and a short lecture. At the close of the first meeting a newcomer is assigned to one of the old members who attempts to explain more clearly the methods of treatment and urges the patient to return to the next meeting. After attending the second meeting the patient acquires "membership."

To each member a seat is assigned according to the number of meetings he has attended. The new members sit in the rear. They move forward as their record of attendance increases. Each member is supposed to find his proper place. For example: A member who has five credits sits to the left of one who has six credits and to the right of one who has only four credits. With each meeting they move towards the front, and thus are brought more and more conspicuously to the attention of the doctor and social worker who sit on the platform. At the opening of the meeting the roll is called; thus the members learn each other's names.

This is followed by a period of muscular and mental relaxation. The patients are instructed to close their eyes and to relax one group of muscles after the other until the entire body is made limp. All who have succeeded are asked to raise their right hand

148

while continuing to keep their eyes closed. Then the patients are asked to picture before their minds a lake in the wilderness on a quiet summer afternoon with its surface as smooth as a mirror. The aim is to have the surface of their consciousness unruffled by a single troubled thought. After silently dwelling on this image for about 30 seconds, the patients are asked to raise their right hand if they feel mentally quiet. With eyes closed, nearly everyone present raises a hand.

After this exercise a short lecture of from 10-15 minutes is given, and largely addressed to the newcomers. This lecture period is followowd by testimonials from members, but only three or four are called upon to explain how the application of what they have learned has improved their health. No one is allowed to talk about difficulties not overcome or to talk about failures.

The "Classes in Applied Psychology" are given to non-psychotic patients, but I believe that we psychiatrists, too, may learn from Dr. Pratt's techniques in our "Group Psychotherapy" sessions. It may be of added historical interest to know that more than 100 years ago a sort of group therapy had been practiced by some superintendents of mental institutions by having patients attend dinner under the supervision and guidance of the superintendent, thus allowing free communications and improved socialization. This, I believe, could also be called a precursor of our present day group psychotherapy.

DISCUSSION OF DR. ROBERTS' PAPER

Dr. Max Fink:—

The distinction between group therapy and group meetings has been made clear. The various discussants have noted that considerable information can be obtained in group therapy sessions by observing the behavior of the patients as they accept their seats in the room. For the past year, Dr. Joseph Jaffe has been recording these patient movements and has reported that patients express their transference feelings by the distance from the therapist's chair. Since these patients are being seen in individual

149

therapy as well, he has made a point of using such information when it seemed advisable.

I am reminded about the unconscious motivations in choice of occupation when we here express the awareness that many of the psychiatric residents are acutely uncomfortable when they have to deal with more than one person at a time. It is no accident that we as a group have no representative who is in a primarily psychoanalytic life experience. The discomfort of psychiatrists when assuming the group role can probably be minimized by experience and training. We at Hillside have had four senior psychiatrists come to us from the Menninger Foundation during the past five or six years, and each has been exemplary in his ability and interest in group behavior. I believe that participation by residents in ward meetings should be made an essential part of the training program.

CHANGING RELATION OF THE PATIENT, FAMILY AND PRACTICING PSYCHIATRIST TO THE THERAPEUTIC COMMUNITY

Alexander Gralnick, M.D., F.A.P.A.

Having come through several decades of rather productive changes, we are currently living in the midst of exciting times within our specialty. The introduction of insulin therapy (1) infused us with an optimism from which we have never quite receded. It is true that innovations have arrived with such frequency since then that there has not been time to return to any degree of lethargy or pessimism. Electroshock therapy (2) aroused any flagging enthusiasm which may have stolen upon us when insulin therapy did not continue to meet up to our anticipations, as did its various modifications, and combinations of it with insulin coma treatment. Metrazol convulsive therapy had already come and gone, and carbon dioxide inhalation therapy and intra venous ether drip therapy also saw their day, and night. Where the effects of the physiological procedure itself did not seem sufficient to explain the improvement in patients, additional psychotherapeutic aspects of them were described (3-8).

Cerebral surgery entered the picture to handle those patients who did not respond to our numerous ministrations, but instead remained the dregs of a rather bitter cup. Psychosurgery became our answer to the remnant of psychotics who resisted our march forward, and frustrated our ego satisfaction. Then, as though there could be sensed some seed of misgiving with the results of these procedures, the drug therapies came upon the scene. And now, psychopharmacology (9) is all the rage, and miracle drugs, tranquilizers and psychic energizers command our attention as we coin new words to explain our new comprehension, cover our yet remaining ignorance, or mask our chagrin.

As though all of this were not enough, we have also had our share of innovations on the non-physiological side. Witness the changing attitudes in psychoanalysis (10) and the increasing influence of allied disciplines in psychiatry. The growth of group therapy and family therapy (11) are also illustrative, as is the growing field of psychosomatic medicine. The increasing tendency to ambulate patients as rapidly as possible is in part a response to economic pressures, but also an evidence of belief in its preferability to inpatient care. In other words, the patient is thought to be benefited if he is out of the hospital as soon as possible. The

153

growth of psychiatric units within general hospitals is an obvious response to economic factors, and to the belief that patients should be brought closer to medicine, to the family and community. Such innovations as the day-hospital, night-hospital and the open door policy are similar evidences of our efforts to improve treatment of the mentally ill. Although the above list is by no means complete, we may add "and now lastly the concept of the therapeutic community" which, although not an entirely new idea, seems to be coming increasingly to the fore (12-15).

At various stages of his knowledge man deals with problems differently. He has not always treated the mentally ill by institutionalization as he has in the last century or so. At first we hospitalized the patient to merely remove him from society and prevent him from doing injury. It is true that the early primitive methods were supplanted by more humane attitudes and procedures, perhaps to compensate the poor inmate for that of which he had been deprived, and possibly to assuage our own guilt feelings for denying him society's pleasures. This did not indicate that we believed the kindlier treatment necessarily had therapeutic value.

In more recent years we have devoted our major attention to active treatment, research and theory. Essentially this has meant an acting upon the patient through some type of physiological procedure designed to restore his equilibrium. In some instances, intervention has been principally through psychotherapy, with the physiological actually subordinated to it.

As horizons have been expanded we have come to look upon the hospital not as "good" or "bad" in which the "right" or "wrong" treatment is given, but as a community with its own social structure. As such, it immediately suggests overtones of a therapeutic nature. In such a setting all of the participants take on a human quality, that of interacting beings who affect each other in a vital way. Much more is involved than the mere giving of a drug or application of a procedure, and the doctor is more than a technician. He too is not exempt from scrutiny, and his personal qualities and emotions become as significant as his knowledge and ability.

154

The relation of the patient, family and referring psychiatrist to the hospital has been rather well known. Essentially the patient has been the unwilling participant, committed by legal means, ejected from his social setting to become a cog in the machinery of the large institution, and acted upon by doctors in an effort to repair him so that he may be restored to society. If occupied during his stay it is with the object of keeping him busy and out of mischief. Therapeutic aspects of such occupation are in terms of ego satisfaction in manual accomplishments and competitive sports, or in terms of improvement automatic to mental diversion.

By and large, the patient's family has had little significant relationship to the institution. Essentially the relative has been a source of historical information, a visitor, and perhaps the haven to whom the doctor will return the patient. This has been true for two likely reasons. First, that staff shortages have made it impossible to devote much time to the relative, and second, that our basic theory has branded him the villain of the piece. Consequently, he is separated off from the patient and a certain degree of ill-will is borne him by the psychiatrist in the protective role he assumes vis-a-vis the patient. For both reasons, of course, the psychiatrist's experience in developing an active role for the relative has been limited, and his ability to integrate him into the therapeutic program has been kept at a minimum. Freud has expressed our general despair in this area by stating, "As for treatment of the relative I must confess myself utterly at a loss, and I have altogether little faith in any individual treatment of them" (16). However, more recently, a more optimistic and realistic approach to the family is being taken as we develop our thinking about the therapeutic community (17-19).

The bulk of psychiatrists in the community has had the barest relationship to the mental institution, other than to recommend hospitalization when they can no longer manage patients otherwise. In most cases such recommendation is made under emergency rather than elective conditions. The usual conscientious doctor dislikes giving up, and perhaps admitting defeat. In psychiatry particularly we look upon separating the patient from his physician as especially traumatic, and therefore inadvisable. This too would encourage the therapist to cling to the bitter end. Naturally, the crowded conditions, poor staffing, and limited therapeutic program of our institutions have not given the practicing psychiatrist much encouragement to advise hospitalization too readily. His attitude toward the hospital psychiatrist is perhaps a factor too. Of course, the public's attitude toward hospitalization, and the patient's resistance to it, constantly limit the psychiatrist from advising it any too soon. It is a fact too that the criteria for recommending hospitalization are not any too clear. Most unfortunate is the fact that once hospitalized, contact between patient and therapist is generally completely severed, although in some cases this may be a good thing. Basically then, a vacuum exists between the private psychiatrist and the mental institution.

When we think of the hospital as a therapeutic community we tend to emphasize the significance of its social structure as a therapeutic force. This concept suggests that treatment procedures and drugs do not alone make the advanced hospital, but that the nature of the social relationships existing therein are perhaps quite as important (20-22). If we are to understand the significance of the therapeutic community we must first attempt its adequate description.

It is taken for granted firstly that the therapeutic community will adequately tend to the physical and physiological requirements of its patients. Over and above this, however, the basic approach of its medical staff toward mental disease will be most important. The physician will treat the patient as a person who has a disease. He will not be treating a disease within a patient. With this approach the needs of the individual as such, and the group of which he is a part, will receive equitable management, as their interests tend to clash. The team-approach would also seem to be an integral part of a therapeutic community, as would the opportunity for close relationship between the patient and his therapist. The doctor should have the opportunity to deal with both the therapeutic and administrative aspects of his patient's management. The medical staff, dynamically oriented, should make hospital and therapeutic policy. Patients should have an opportunity to work closely together in activities designed to contribute to the social setting in which they are living. The units of a therapeutic community will have to be small if an atmosphere of intimacy is to develop. Policy should be flexible and designed to meet changing conditions, and means of communication among patients, and between patients and staff, should be of the best (23). Value judgments must find a place in the therapeutic community if structure and order in its social relationships is to be maintained.

THE THERAPEUTIC COMMUNITY

It is a social structure with its own particular ways and laws, and is not to be confused with a setting in which one has freedom to do as he pleases without restriction. It has conscious design, and its main aim is to help the patient to become a more mature and rational person, not merely as well as he once was. It is not necessarily designed for speed of recovery and to meet the requirements of limited budgets.

Although the concept and the full description of the therapeutic community have yet to be detailed, we know enough to realize that all concerned are faced with changing relationships to the mental institution. The hospital psychiatrist has been facing this wherever his organization has been moving in the new direction. But what of the others?

When the prospective patient realizes that in the newer atmosphere he is a respected individual of the hospital community, not "the patient" and that he has a significant role in its fabric, he will be more apt to accept hospitalization. It may be expected too that he will welcome staying in the more wholesome atmosphere which offers him more promise, and gain the most from what it has to offer him. We may anticipate further that the changed conditions will help dissipate the feelings of shame and of social stigma which surround hospitalization today. Above all, the patient should have a much healthier respect for the hospital and fellow patients, and be a contributing participant to its welfare, even perhaps after he has left its confines (24).

It is likely that the true therapeutic community will enlist the relative more actively in its program (25). Signs of this are already evident in the group meetings being held with relatives. Authority figures within the hospital will establish parental relationships to patients. Under such conditions they will develop more sympathetic understanding of the problems of the true parents and relatives. Working relationships between therapist and relatives on behalf of the patient should then improve. More wholesome attitudes on the part of relatives toward our institutions should encourage them to influence governmental agencies in favor of better treatment and research programs. In the therapeutic community the therapist will give the relative more understanding of psychopathology so that he may more thoroughly comprehend the patient. Relatives will appreciate this and in turn will be seen as less villainous.

As mental institutions have become more active treatment centers the practicing psychiatrist has increasingly viewed them with favor. Any reservations have been a reflection of the manner in which patients as people are treated because of overcrowded conditions. Among other things, the rapid growth of small psychiatric units within general hospitals is a sign of such dissatisfaction. In such units the practicing psychiatrist maintains closer and continuing contact with his patient in a more wholesome setting. It is to be expected, however, that as our institutions develop into therapeutic communities the psychiatrist will alter his attitudes, and thereby help affect the negative attitudes of the public. It is to be hoped that he may take a more active role in both the training and treatment programs of our larger institutions, and thereby promote their growth into better therapeutic communities. The practicing psychiatrist's participation in the treatment of hospitalized patients may ultimately be considered an ingredient of the therapeutic community concept. There was a time when state institutions were quite isolated geographically. What must be overcome now is the emotional isolation in which they have been maintained. At any rate, the practicing psychiatrist is faced with an increasing challenge as the therapeutic community develops within institutions.

We are living in a time when great pressures, emotional and economic, are being exerted to have us produce quick results in psychiatry. Progress is being measured by the rapidity with which we can get patients out of our hospitals, as if being out is the sine qua non of being well. It would be as though some magic is worked once a patient walks out of the front door of an institution, or some worthy service is done the patient if he is saved from entering a hospital, no matter how long he may otherwise be kept in a state of imbalance or unresolved conflict. Improved mental health in a community seems to be measured by a decreasing state budget and the brevity of the average hospital stay.

Under such conditions perspective and the true interest of science may be easily lost. We do not tend to engage in this type of thinking in physical medicine. What if we did with cancer? It is not necessarily serving the best interests of society, or patients themselves to have an increasing number of mentally sick people walking about. Time, of course, will help us with any such evaluation. We may find yet that the answer will remain in relatively long hospitalization, but under the better conditions of a therapeutic community.

Of course, logic would seem to suggest that if mental illness is even in part socially determined (26-29), then favorable results would flow from the more rational social structure of the therapeutic community. Knitting the hospital as such more closely into the larger community would also seem to foretell more favorable results. In many ways, however, the therapeutic community calls for a more complicated social organization for the hospital, with more integrated and complex activity programs of patient participation in the institution's fabric. It may suggest and require longer hospitalizations for the reconstruction of patients. Many may oppose any such trend. It has already been said that activity and occupational programs should be cut down out of fear that they promote comfort and prolong stays. We should beware of pressures which, in the service of economy, would curtail the logical and scientific growth of the therapeutic community concept. At the same time, caution is needed in evaluating this newer concept of treatment. The "new" is not necessarily the "best" or even the "better." Wholesome development and rational change in our system of hospital treatment would seem necessary, but let us beware of discarding the baby with the bathwater.

SUMMARY AND CONCLUSION

The changing scene in psychiatric hospitals has been described with emphasis on the relationship between psychiatrist, patient and family. It is believed that emphasis must be shifted towards "total" treatment of the patient in an enlightened social setting. Here, active patient participation will be an index of healthy group interaction between various staff members and patients.

The private psychiatrist should be integrated into the hospital activities.

The therapeutic effectiveness of short versus long hospitalization has been considered.

BIBLIOGRAPHY

1. Gralnick, A.: A seven year survey of insulin treatment in schizophrenia. *Am. J. Psychiat., 101:* 449, 1945.
2. Gralnick, A.: A three year survey of electroshock therapy: Report on 276 cases; comparative value of insulin coma therapy. *Am. J. Psychiat., 102:* 583, 1946.
3. Gralnick, A.: Psychotherapeutic and interpersonal aspects of insulin treatment. *Psychiat. Quart., 18:* 179, 1944.
4. Kalinowsky, L. B.: Problems of psychotherapy and transference in shock treatments and psychosurgery. *Psychosom. Med., 18:* 399, 1956.
5. Hill, L. B., and Patton, J. D.: When physical therapy (shock) facilitates psychotherapy. *Am. J. Psychiat., 113:* 60, 1956.
6. Silverberg, W. V., and Hirning, L. D.: Psychotherapy and adjunctive means in psychiatry. *Am. J. Psychother., 12:* 760, 1958.
7. Rabiner, E. L., and Gralnick, A.: Transference and countertransference phenomena in the choice of shock therapy: A review of 100 cases with a comparative study. *A.M.A. Arch. Neurol. Psychiat.* In press.
8. Gralnick, A.: *Adjunctive Shock Treatment in an Intensive Psychotherapeutic Program.* 2nd International Congress of Psychiatry, Vol. 2, pg. 380, Zurich, Orell, Füssli Arts Graphiques, 1959.

9. Kline, N.S., Ed.: *Psychopharmacology Frontiers*. Boston, Little, Brown & Co., 1959.

10. Mohr, G. J.: *Psychoanalysis: Some Present Day Assessments*. Academy of Psychoanalysis, New York, 1958.

11. Ackerman, N. W.: Toward an integrative therapy of the family. *Am. J. Psychiat., 114:* 727, 1958.

12. MacDonald, J. M., and Daniels, M. L.: The psychiatric ward as a therapeutic community. *J. Nerv. Ment. Dis., 124:* 148, 1956.

13. Jones, M.: The treatment of personality disorders in a therapeutic community. *Psychiatry, 20:* 211, 1957.

14. Wilmer, H. A.: Toward a definition of the therapeutic community. *Am. J. Psychiat., 114:* 824, 1958.

15. Gralnick, A.: Behavioral determinants in a therapeutic milieu. In: *The Dynamics of Psychiatric Drug Therapy*. Ed. Sarwer-Foner, G. J., Springfield, Charles C Thomas, 1959. In press.

16. Freud, S.: Recommendations for physicians on the psychoanalytic method of treatment. *Collected Papers, 2:* 323, London, Hogarth Press, 1933.

17. Hall, B. H., and Wheeler, W.: The patient and his relatives. *Social Work, 2:* 75, 1957.

18. Lefebvre, P., Atkins, J., Duckman, J. and Gralnick, A.: The role of the relative in a psychotherapeutic program. *J. Canad. Psychiat. Assoc., 3:* 110, 1958.

19. Gralnick, A.: The family in psychotherapy. In: *Individual and Family Dynamics*. Ed. Masserman, J., New York, Grune & Stratton, 1959.

20. Gralnick, A., Schacht, M., and Kempster, S. W.: Psychotherapy in a private mental hospital. *Am. J. Psychoth., 8:* 312, 1954.

21. Starr, A., and Gralnick, A.: Factors determining the initial effect of hospitalization on cases of schizophrenia. *Am. J. Psychoth., 9:* 243, 1955.

22. Cohen, R. A.: The hospital as a therapeutic instrument. *Psychiatry, 21:* 29, 1958.

23. O'Connor, W., Carstairs, G. M., and Rawnsley, K.: Communication in a mental hospital population. *Int. J. Soc. Psychiat., 3:* 183, 1957.

24. Gralnick, A., and D'Elia, F.: *Role of the Patient in the Therapeutic Community: Patient-participation.* Southern Divisional Meeting, American Psychiatric Assoc., Miami, 1958.

25. Gralnick, A.: Relation of the family to a psychotherapeutic inpatient program. *Int. J. Soc. Psychiat.* In press.

26. Gralnick, A.: Folie à deux—The psychosis of association. *Psychiat. Quart., 16:* 230 and 491, 1942.

27. Gralnick, A.: The Carrington family: A psychiatric and social study illustrating the psychosis of association or folie à deux. *Psychiat. Quart., 17:* 294, 1943.

28. Gruenberg, E. M.: Socially shared psychopathology. In: *Explorations in Social Psychiatry,* New York, Basic Books, 1958.

29. Redlich, F. D.: Social aspects of psychotherapy in the United States. *Progress in Psychotherapy, 3:* 79, 1958, New York, Grune & Stratton.

DISCUSSION OF DR. GRALNICK'S PAPER

Dr. Max Fink:—

I would agree that there is no one "therapeutic community" but that all hospital aggregates are "communities" and the therapeutic element is a matter of degree. This conference has as a title a single concept, "Therapeutic Community" and I would like to change it to "Therapeutic Communities." The discussion today, I believe, has suffered from a lack of discrimination of the individual differences in population. It seems as if the recommendations for one population should be applicable to another. But this is not true. The experiments of Drs. Sullivan and Freida Fromm-Reichman were limited to severe schizophrenic patients. Other discussants have described groups which are differently constituted, such as the emphasis on psychopathic personalities in the Jones' community or the chronic group of patients seen at Boston Psychopathic. I would like to make a plea that the discussion be focused on some of the differences in population and the extent to which such differences affect the ability with which such changes in milieu augment or depress therapeusis.

THE DAY HOSPITAL
AS A THERAPEUTIC COMMUNITY

T. J. Boag, M. B., Ch.B.

INTRODUCTION

The first Day Hospital, as so designated, was set up in the Allan Memorial Institute in 1946 (1). Ten years later, in spite of a great deal of experience and oft repeated demonstrations of its usefulness, we experienced increasing difficulties in its operation. This led to a reorganization in the course of which some basic premises underlying management of this setting were reformulated, and a programme of group activities introduced with the purpose of structuring the milieu in accordance with our reformulation. This paper will describe these reforms and the changes which followed.

The Day Hospital is part of the Allan Memorial Institute which is, itself, part of a general hospital. The Institute is entirely open. It has a total of 89 in-patient beds so that with 40 places, the Day Hospital is a large part of our resources. In contrast to some other centres, only about one-quarter of our Day Hospital patients have been transferred from the in-patient side. We do not regard it as a half-way house but as one resource amongst others, with its own sphere of usefulness; patients are transferred quite actively in and out of it according to their current requirements. All forms of physical treatment are available except deep coma insulin. Patients are not selected in terms of diagnosis. The principal criteria are their ability to travel, and the feasibility of their continuing to live at home during treatment. At times when there is a large waiting list for in-patient beds, we have to treat some extremely disturbed patients. As well as drawing on the general resources of the Institute, clinical responsibility for patients is divided among four Public Services, each of which has patients on all wards including the Day Hospital. This division of medical responsibility for the group as a whole, means that the nurses on the Day Hospital occupy a central position in its social structure (2).

When opened in 1946 there was space for 20 patients, and this expanded to 40 in 1954. In the spring of 1958 there was an extensive reorganization, integrating within the Day Hospital a wide range of ambulant facilities which had developed independently. This provided an extremely adaptable treatment area in which all standard forms of treatment were available on a scale of frequency and intensity ranging from full-time Day Hospital attendance (9 a.m. to 5 p.m., six days weekly) to an occasional single visit. This reorganization will be described elsewhere (3), and in this paper I shall concentrate on one aspect concerning the core group of 40 full-time Day Hospital patients, and will describe how we became interested in the Day Hospital as a therapeutic milieu, attempted to define what its characteristics should be, and tried to structure the setting accordingly.

METHOD

The reorganization in January 1958 was precipitated by increasing operational difficulties of the Day Hospital as it then existed. This was due to a complex of factors, many of them beyond our control, e. g., the fiscal policies of hospitalization plans. However, it was clear that among the factors within our control was a failure to organize a milieu which met the needs of these patients. Psychiatrists were hesitant to refer patients, and many patients were reluctant to enter or, once there, to stay. They felt that not requiring 24 hour care, they should be treated in a clinic rather than "sitting around all day doing nothing." This reflected their difficulty in reconciling the novel setting with an orthodox conception of a "hospital." It also reflected our failure to formulate a specific Day Hospital programme offering something more than out-patient treatment in a clinic, and yet different from residence in an in-patient ward.

We, therefore, became concerned with the Day Hospital as a treatment setting, how this could be made more "therapeutic," and how a therapeutic setting could be provided that was different from the in-patient or out-patient services. Finally we were concerned with staff contribution to the maintenance of this setting; it being clear that this would fall mainly on the nursing staff, being the only representatives of the hospital as a treatment institution constantly present in the Day Hospital. Obviously, however, many other people could be brought in as auxiliaries.

Whatever other functions might be served by the Day Hospital, it had also to serve as a setting for traditional "medical" investiga-

166

tion and treatment, with provision of nursing care, proper supervision of physical treatments, and distribution of drugs. This was necessary not only because many patients were treated in these ways in addition to other therapeutic efforts, but also because there was always a certain number of patients who were seriously disturbed, confused and awaiting in-patient beds. These activities fostered the development of a dependent relationship to the hospital and its representatives. This cannot be avoided and is a necessary part of such a treatment setting. To a certain extent it is desirable. However, unless considerable attention is devoted to fostering other forms of activity, this is liable to represent the main and only attitude of the hospital to which the patient is exposed. It carries considerable implications for him in terms of his own attitudes towards his problems, his treatment, the doctors, the hospital, etc. In other words, the danger is of an excessive provocation of regression, passive resistance, demanding attitudes, seeking of direction and medication. This counters the patient's own potentialities for solving his problems and for the development of progressive defenses rather than such regressive ones. We, therefore, felt that although the provision of support, care, medicine and "oral supplies" in general was a legitimate background for the provision of other forms of treatment, we should try to provide them only to the degree necessary to relieve anxiety, foster the development of progressive defenses, and minimize dependency. It was clear that in the past, when other activities on the ward were deficient, such dependency was very much encouraged. The sort of thing that happened was that a patient would spend most of the day sitting alone or with one or two cronies, punctuating this by attendance at the door of the nurses' office to receive pills, reassurance, advice, etc. Alternatively, if these demands were frustrated, they would adjourn to the coffee shop to air their grievances against the hospital and nurses. Therefore, we decided to start with the working assumption that for the majority of patients referred to the Day Hospital, the development of multiple object relations within a group, varying in type, was not only possible, but was also therapeutically desirable. It followed that development of a strong democratic group structure on the ward was eminently desirable in order to foster progressive attitudes and defenses. This was laid down as the first aim of our programme.

Group activities related to progressive, independent functioning, aimed away from the hospital and towards a return to normal life, were to be encouraged. This meant establishing communal activities carried out by the patient group as a whole so that a structured group could, in fact, develop.

Secondly, adequate opportunities must be given for the subsequent group interactions to be verbalized. The patients had to meet as a discussion group sufficiently regularly, that the minutiae of daily interaction were expressed and discussed.

The third requirement was that staff members concerned should contribute in such a way as to foster desirable attitudes to the group interactions. The attitudes to be expressed were— 1) support and encouragement toward rehabilitation, return to work, return to independent functioning, etc., 2) adoption of what might be called a "psychological" attitude, i. e., perceiving the daily interactions on the ward as an acting-out of internalized pre-existing conflicts. This was analogous to a similar acting-out in other previous life situations.

The fourth requirement was for provision of facilities which patients could utilize to work through their problems towards reality solutions. These included special groups devoted to questions of employment, family relationships, provision of information on social techniques, films providing psychological information followed by discussion, etc. In addition to special groups specifically provided in the Day Hospital, there were, of course, many other resources of the hospital which could be utilized at this stage, e.g., individual psychotherapy, long-term intensive group psychotherapy on an out-patient basis, individual case work in the Social Service Department, resources of the Occupational Therapy Department, etc.

Implementation of a programme in accordance with these general aims essentially took the form of a range of group activities. They were planned to fit the four stages described above, and also

168

to give a shape to the life of the patients in the Day Hospital in terms of their daily movements in space and in time.

First in importance was the discussion hour when all patients met daily from 1 to 2 p.m. The main responsibility for this lay with the nurses and particularly with the head nurse. She is the main focus of the social structure of the ward and must head the group if it is to be a part of the social reality of life on the Day Hospital. A part of this reality rests on issues being made overt and tackled on a cooperative rational basis. If it functions properly, this should be a forum in which consciousness of the group structure is mainly developed and where most of the preliminary verbalizations take place. They must meet daily so that discussion of intellectual generalizations cannot be maintained but minutiae of the daily interactions on the Day Hospital are necessarily expressed and discussed. It became apparent to both patients and nurses that certain problems could be discussed more easily in groups consisting of men or women only. The "Men's Group" and "Women's Group" emerged from this, each meeting once weekly as, in effect, a sub-committee of the main ward discussion group.

To help emotional expression and discussion of significant problems, all patients participated in a weekly sociodrama session conducted by our group worker, acting out real situations from home or the ward. Thus, considerable feed-back developed to the discussion groups. Another technique, more neutral perhaps, was the showing of psychiatric films for patients not ready to deal with the direct impact of current reality situations. Each was followed by a discussion period. Again much of the value of this lay in the feed-back to other discussion groups.

A number of special groups dealing with the fourth stage (working toward reality solutions) met regularly. Our Social Service Department took over this responsibility, and the groups were led by social workers. Each group dealt with a special problem, e.g., work, family life, etc., and patients were referred on the basis of individual suitability. The emphasis was on maintaining an orientation toward rehabilitation and return to a normal life. Discussion and interpretation included both intrapsychic and reality difficulties inherent in the current social situation. For instance, the "Work Group" discussed patients' attitudes and conflicts to work, the meaning of work in our society, current difficulties in obtaining employment, etc. A special employment counsellor, who came to the hospital once weekly from the National Employment Service, at first sat in on this group as a consultant, and later took over as its leader. Another group was oriented toward discussion of family problems; a third was designed specifically for patients who had experienced major isolation and was directed to social activities and clubs.

The so-called "Lectures in Living" were given on another afternoon each week by well-known recognized local authorities who were invited to speak on a wide variety of subjects, such as budget planning, running a house, learning to paint, etc. This was followed by occupational therapy when they aroused a latent interest in the patients, and later linked to continued training after discharge.

In addition to these specific group activities we enlisted the help of the occupational therapists in developing recreational activities on the ward and activities utilizing the resources of the Occupational Therapy Department. Here we were concerned with structuring the day and with the offering of new opportunities for sublimations in patients who were now showing new and progressive adaptations.

EFFECTS OF THE PROGRAMME

The formal activities set up served as a framework within which growth and development could occur. As an active community came into life on the Day Hospital, the skeleton was fleshed out by more and more spontaneous activity set up informally by the patients. As their projects became more complex, they developed formal social structures, e.g., electing ad hoc committees, and involving the staff as well. The skeleton itself, of course, could not

170

remain a rigid and unchanging structure, but has continued to change in accordance with needs, as the community developed a life and drive of its own.

The evaluation of the full effects of such a program is complex and would require much time. There has been a vast improvement in overall morale on the Day Hospital including both patients and staff. This is expressed by both groups and evidenced by the general level of activity, including the spontaneous development of activities organized by the patients themselves. There has been a rapid upsurge of referrals so that the Day Hospital has usually been full and frequently had a waiting list. Referring psychiatrists have found the programme much more useful in that the individual patient can find the activities he needs at a given time. The Day Hospital has become much more useful in active rehabilitation and the movement of patients from hospital life to home life.

The programme has had its impact on the rest of the hospital. When most active, the Day Hospital has achieved a certain prestige among the other patients which never existed previously. Patients on other wards pressed to take part in these activities and later began to emulate them on their own wards. It has stimulated much interest among the nursing staff on other wards towards better organization and development of ward activities. There has been a very definite drop in anxiety over the possibility of instituting and developing such changes.

Do these changes represent the growth of new elements in the community life which are self-sustaining, and may be expected to survive and grow? So often, in retrospect, it is clear that they are a reaction to the presence of an enthusiast and die out rapidly when he leaves. It is still too soon to evaluate the programme, but certain elements may signify a good prognosis. First, I initiated the changes in January 1958, and severed my connection with the project at the end of the year. After three months the programme is still flourishing. Second, there was a rationale for the changes introduced, and for the means used to achieve the desired ends. Third, new developments have emerged spontaneously, and have involved staff members who were indifferent or openly skeptical.

DISCUSSION

Many of the problems are related to the type of control exerted over patients. It comes up in questions concerned with "responsibility," "freedom," "control," etc. There has been a tendency to express it in terms of black and white. As if on one side we have patients who are responsible, who are free, who in general terms are called "neurotic" and on whom we need not exert any control, while on the other side are patients who are not "responsible," could not not be allowed freedom and tend to be labeled "schizophrenic." This kind of dichotomy is reflected in the patterns of psychiatric practice in North America (4).

The dichotomy is, of course, an artificial simplification. The phenomena are more accurately represented on a continuum. We have for years thought of the responsibility of our patients for their actions in relative terms, although the conflict of this with older and simpler concepts still gives rise to difficulties in dealing with legal problems. It does not seem too much to ask that we should begin to think of the problem of controls also in relative terms. We are naive if we imagine that we do not exert some form of control on a patient as soon as we see him, whether this is accounted for by the rational acceptance of the patient-doctor relationship or by transference components in the relationship. Between this and the other extreme of depriving a patient of his civil rights and locking him up, there are many possible degrees ranging through social controls of behavior, drugs, and other forms of therapy.

Our first problem in modifying therapeutic settings is to undo the ill-effects of the past methods of handling patients. There is a mass of evidence that a very high proportion of patients do not need to be treated in closed settings as in the past. The large locked custodial hospital has played an important part in producing the picture of chronic deteriorated backward patients. We have to substitute other forms of control, social, pharmacological, etc., so that new and different settings may be devised which minimize the effects of unnecessary restrictions. The second problem becomes that of structuring our settings so that they make a positive contribution to the attainment of our therapeutic goals. It is against a wider canvas such as this that we must view the small experiment I have described, and the many others which are now in progress in North America and Europe.

SUMMARY AND CONCLUSION

A description has been given of the varied activities and purposes of the Day Hospital Division. The group activities are all interlinked and contribute to the therapeutic atmosphere. Much importance is attached to the staff's active participation.

Progressive changes are taking place from custodial to therapeutic orientations with restructuring of the hospital environment. The Day Hospital represents an advance in this direction.

BIBLIOGRAPHY

1. Cameron, D. E.: The day hospital. *Modern Hospital, 69:* 3, 1947.

2. Boag, T. J.: The role of the psychiatric nurse working on the day hospital. *Proceedings of Conference for Psychiatric Nurses in General Hospitals.* In press.

3. Boag, T. J.: *Further Developments in the Day Hospital.* American Psychiatric Association, Philadelphia, April 28, 1959.

4. MacIver, J., and Redlich, F. C.: Patterns of psychiatric practice. *Am. J. Psychiat., 115:* 8, 1959.

DISCUSSION OF DR. BOAG'S PAPER

DR. C. CONWAY SMITH:—

On the fourth floor of the new Montreal General Hospital there is located a treatment unit, the Night Centre, which begins its work at a time when most facilities are closing for the day. Here one may find professional men and women, husbands, wives, unskilled laborers, and in fact, any person. This unit was designed to furnish psychiatric help to those individuals who for financial or other reasons could not afford to take time off for partial day time or total hospitalization. It offers early treatment to thos with non-psychotic psychiatric disorders.

The Night Centre is located in the Department of Psychiatry of the recently built Montreal General Hospital with facilities for male and female patients. Modified insulin, sub-shock, and electroconvulsive treatments are given in addition to psychotherapy which is received by all patients. Those receiving modified insulin come to the hospital at 6:00 P. M. and remain until 7:00 A. M the following morning, from Monday through Friday, inclusive.

Patients receiving the electric therapies in general do not remain overnight; but return to their homes usually no later than 9:00 P. M. Individual psychotherapeutic sessions are arranged with psychiatrists for all patients while they are receiving physi cal treatments. Some patients, on the other hand, receive only individualized psychotherapy.

The professional staff consists of a psychiatrist, post-graduate nurse trained in psychiatry, and four to five residents. Weekly staff conferences are held by the entire Night Centre professional staff, where observations of the nurses and psychiatrists are reviewed. Each patient's progress is followed constantly, therefore from the moment of admission until after discharge. All patients are thoroughly screened for physical illness prior to their treatment and any physical disability is treated.

The Night Centre has now been in function for approximately three years. During this time it has played a very useful role in the community, serving the following functions:—

1. Psychiatric treatment is made available to patients without interfering with their daily work.

2. It has provided a system of treatment in which the individual is able to continue to function in reality. This in itself is conducive to increased feelings of security, financial as well as emotional.

174

3. By allowing the patient to daily maintain usual interpersonal relationships, regression, as it is usually met within a hospital setting is markedly reduced.

4. Psychiatric treatment is available to the patient with psychoneurotic, psychosomatic and prepsychotic symptoms at a time when therapy can be most effective; namely, before the patient becomes so incapacitated as to necessitate prolonged hospitalization. Depression, anxiety reaction, phobias, and schizophrenic reaction are typical of the emotional disturbances treated.

5. It allows the earning power of the family to remain intact, as well as providing a stable family throughout the treatment time.

6. The cost to the patient for hospitalization and treatment is considerably less in the Night Centre than on a 24 hour basis.

7. The patients have felt less stigmatized by their illness and they are observed to continue functioning by their employers, friends and immediate family.

This service has continued most active throughout the years from its inception, and has become the model for similar treatment plans in hospitals in many parts of the world. It would appear that in the years to come the role of a night psychiatric treatment unit will continue to be firmly established.

DISCUSSION OF DR. BOAG'S PAPER

Dr. Leigh M. Roberts:—

The presentation of the day hospital as a therapeutic community outlines well many aspects of hospital milieu therapy. Though a specialized situation, it is not markedly different in many areas from some state hospital environments where similar programs have evolved. The efforts to maximally utilize nursing staff leadership may help to overcome the problem of dependency of the treatment approach on the presence of individual physicians who lead it. Whether this will permit it to be more self-perpetuating or not may be answered by the dispersion of active leadership on many staff members. The caliber of leadership continues to represent a nucleus within the community and on this to a sizeable extent hinges the degree of success. The training, sensitivity and skill of the leader are major elements in their effectiveness in that role and it is possible to assign leadership roles to various staff members regardless of their previous professional training if they possess some of the natural qualities needed and can receive the desired training. The role of leadership may not, however, be effectively assigned in an arbitrary way to staff members without these considerations.

ADOLESCENT PAVILION —
HILLSIDE HOSPITAL

Simon Kwalwasser, M.D.

INTRODUCTION

The therapeutic community known as the Israel Strauss Adolescent Pavilion for Girls at Hillside Hospital, Glen Oaks, New York, was formally opened in October 1954. It was designed as an intensive, individualized, dynamically oriented treatment program in a group setting. While intensive psychotherapy was the core of treatment, all the ancillary services were integrated by the therapist into a continuous living experience so that each thing the patient did was considered in terms of its value to the overall treatment.

In this setting, one must take into account the daily group experience of the patient. One of the prime functions in the establishment of a therapeutic community of this type was to enable each member of the staff to vividly see his contribution in relation to all other staff members, to the total program and goals of treatment. Proper appreciation and respect for the contributions of non-medical staff is an essential part of the total rehabilitative experience. Psychotherapy means not only understanding what the patient says at an interview, but understanding of the patient's functioning with all other people in her environment.

The original goal at the Adolescent Pavilion was to treat with a highly structured and intensively supportive therapeutic program: 1) adolescent girls between the ages of 13 and 16 who were going through an acute period of crisis which required separation from home, and 2) patients capable of responding to such treatment within one to one and one-half years, and then continuing on an out-patient basis with either their own therapist or with our aftercare clinic for as long as necessary.

The Adolescent Pavilion was viewed as a pilot study at Hillside Hospital. It, therefore, had considerable flexibility as to what facilities would be used within the hospital and within the community. Some of our original ideas have had to be modified because of the unavailability, at first, of the type of patient we were seeking, as well as the paucity of facilities on the outside.

179

On the other hand, there were many facilities which we did find available in the community—the 600 Program of the Public School System of New York City.* We were allowed to use some of the classes and recreational facilities of the local public school. The community supplied volunteers who helped with instruction in dancing, music, cooking and hair dressing. Others would occasionally invite girls to their homes.

The focal point was psychotherapy by each girl's physician. However, highly disturbed adolescents were in great need of those activities which help to remove the particularly stubborn barriers that interfered seriously with psychotherapeutic accessibility in the early period of hospitalization. Conventional psychotherapy came to be meaningful very slowly to these girls, only as certain fundamental physical and emotional needs were properly and adequately provided for. These needs could only be met by an adequate team approach in which each member of the group had a definite feeling as to his use and value in the overall creation of a healthful and constructive climate in which some of the inner tensions of the girls could be drained off.

In determining the adjunctive activities program there were certain things that had to be taken into consideration—needs and ages of the young versus the older adolescents, compatibility of different age groups living together and the goals of treatment. Since we were dealing with adolescents who were of school age, the learning and cognitive functions had to be very seriously considered.

While schooling was a very important and major part of the program, the basic arrangements of the adjunctive activities program included occupational therapy for creative expression, group work and the social service program, psychological studies, as well as nursing and psychiatric aide care.

It should be mentioned here again before going into details about the various departments, that psychotherapy in this setting

---

* Schools with the 600 Series in New York are those reserved for children with severe emotional disorders.

means the constant awareness on the part of the patient's doctor as to what is going on in the patient's life 24 hours a day in relation to the people around her and the dynamic understanding of what was happening rather than dependence on what the patient might have to say in the "hour."

Prior to the opening of the Adolescent Pavilion, arrangements were made with the Department of Education, City of New York, for two teachers to be provided from their 600 Program. Originally we thought it desirable to have classrooms in the Adolescent Pavilion building itself, but lacking space it was necessary to look elsewhere on the grounds. This gave the feeling of "going to school," for by leaving the Adolescent Pavilion in the morning the patients went about a block or two away within the hospital grounds to the school area.

During the early part of the Pavilion program the possibility of having some of our patients attend school in the local community was tried. At first this program seemed to offer great promise by giving the girls additional contact with the outside and creating a feeling of being less estranged from the community. This was unsuccessful. The present intrahospital school program has the very obvious advantage of having teachers who are aware of each girl's specific emotional problem. The work can be geared to the patient's emotional needs and the atmosphere of the entire classroom setting is more tolerant.

COMPOSITION OF THE GROUP AND TREATMENT DESIGN

A careful selection before admission must operate once a decision is reached as to what type of patient can be treated. Would this be a neurotic, psychotic, delinquent or psychopathic adolescent? Would these patients be able to live together? A careful study was done to determine where these children came from; what kind of parent figures existed; what we could hope to do for them and what arrangements could be made for care prior to admission and after discharge.

181

In the prescreening process it is necessary to determine if we would be able to work with their parents. Some of the girls were treated on a preadmission, out-patient basis with an attempt to provide a general type of emotional support and orientation to the future Pavilion program. They showed sufficient improvement so as not to require hospitalization. Others were too ill, and had to be hospitalized elsewhere.

Much thought was given to the unit's housing arrangements. It was felt that a two-bed room might encourage sexual acting-out, and it was finally decided that a four-bed room would be small enough to be private and yet large enough to prevent too overt acting out. This did not work out according to plan. Four girls in one room proved to be too crowded. It did not even prevent the sexual acting-out. They have now been changed to three-bed rooms. If there were absolutely free choice as to the rooming pattern, we would prefer at present a single room for each girl. These adolescents as a group appear to be too sick to relate positively to each other for any great length of time, especially in enforced closed quarters.

The program must be designed to meet the needs of the group and behavior must in some way be limited. By this we do not mean that the girls must be placed in a strait-jacketed situation, but there must be some definite limitations and structure. They are all patients who have proved by their previous behavior they could not impose limitations upon themselves.

The program design must be such that it affords outlets for the physical and emotional needs in a meaningful and constructive manner. To have no limitations on behavior within the unit would be to invite further acting out with our passive consent.

We have tried to have enough physical education, recreational activities, schooling, seminars in cooking, homemaking and personal grooming that would provide the girls with an image of what it is like to be a healthy woman. We are trying to have mature and desirable adults as part of the therapeutic team to serve as models for these adolescents. The recent introduction

182

of counsellors to the program showed that these more desirable images with whom the girls could identify and feel close to, had a very beneficial effect on the overall results of the entire activities program.

In our project the teachers are regarded as an integral part of the therapeutic community. They meet with all other personnel at staff conferences, have a definite awareness of each girl's problems as well as the problem each girl has with each other member of the team and to her own peers.

The school and occupational therapy programs alternate with each other so that the girls who go to school in the morning go to occupational therapy in the afternoon and vice versa. Emphasis in occupational therapy is on the personal relationship with a therapist who is fully cognizant of the therapeutic goal for each patient and tries to provide an opportunity for this satisfaction.

The Group Activities Department provides for the other group activities, such as music, dancing, physical training and sports, cooking, hair dressing and assisting the girls with their own self-government program. These activities again are planned only as a method of implementing the overall therapeutic goal as carefully conceived and planned by the patient's own doctor.

Social service plays a vital role in the team approach working with the parents, and where desirable, both are seen. Otherwise, one parent is seen on a regular casework basis to assist with interpreting the aims of treatment at the Pavilion during the patient's stay and also with plans for post-hospital care. Social service is concerned in implementing care with other community agencies which may be of assistance to the parents at such time as the patient is in the hospital or with community facilities for the patient when she leaves the hospital.

A psychologist is part of the team. A battery of tests are done on all patients when first admitted. These may be repeated subsequently and are done again prior to discharge. Where vocational guidance and rehabilitation is necessary, he takes a very active part in testing, planning and referral to the appropriate agencies in cooperation with social service.

The nursing department, consisting of nurses and psychiatric aides, has the most intimate contact with patients and many of the programs initiated by occupational therapy and group work activities depend on their assistance. One of the most serious problems in the staffing of the Pavilion was the question of securing proper psychiatric aides, and even before the unit was opened this problem was definitely recognized and discussed.

It was desirable to have people who were in some way interested in working with children. Yet, due to the difficulties in securing adequate personnel, many aides were without special skills or adequate training, acting more like servants, guards and caretakers than active, interested, involved participants. A great deal of time was spent by staff to work with them. While considerable progress was made with some, this remained the most serious weakness in the program. Many were often not able to understand the problems under discussion in the team meetings.

Lately we have been fortunate to find a new type of personnel, whom we have called counsellors, to work with these patients. They are college graduates with special experience in working with children, and have not only added new interests for the girls, but are also much more acceptable ideals to imitate. Patients are sensitive to the attitudes and relationships about them, particularly so in an adolescent unit where they are so much in need of using all the adults about as models for imitations and growth.

THE RELATIONSHIP OF THE ADOLESCENT PAVILION TO THE HOSPITAL AND THE COMMUNITY

When the unit was opened it was first thought of as a highly specialized intensive treatment unit that would function as independently of the remainder of the institution as possible, to have its own specialized personnel carefully screened and indoctrinat-

184

ed with the program and treatment goals and provided with its own activities and recreational program divorced from the adult portion of the hospital.

Our experience with this philosophy turned out to have unexpected negative results. Both patients and employees had a feeling of isolation from the remainder of the hospital. Although often the facilities provided were much better and more elaborate than those provided elsewhere, the patients felt that they were being excluded from the hospital life and were constantly striving to take part in it.

Although their play area was much larger than that provided for the hospital, these 16 girls preferred to have their activities on the same grounds and often at the same time as the adult patients. Not only was there this negative feeling on the part of the patients but an equal feeling of separation amongst the employees. Those who worked in the adult division did not wish to have anything to do with the Adolescent Pavilion and, as they knew very little about it, were extremely reluctant to cover on an emergency basis when the occasion arose.

These attitudes have modified themselves over the past five years. The girls now participate in much of the hospital's recreational activities. While this has created some problems of its own, its benefits far outweigh the negative effects. It has also been necessary to explain more fully the functions and aspirations of the Adolescent Pavilion to the personnel of the entire hospital so as to arouse some interest on their part and to increase their tolerance and understanding. It is now possible to have our employees cover the Pavilion without the old overwhelming anxiety and fear that characterized such earlier requests.

As the facilities of the entire hospital were used, the transfer of a temporarily acutely disturbed girl to the adult portion was tried. While this had some assets, it also had liabilities. Unless handled very tactfully it gave the personnel in the adult section the feeling that the Adolescent Pavilion problem was being side-

185

tracked. While this was not literally true, there can be no doubt that such a possibility affected the attitude and behavior of the personnel in the Pavilion. When there was absolutely nowhere to transfer the girls, they knew that this was a problem that they, themselves, had to handle and solve. We have now limited the possibility of transfer only for therapeutic considerations.

As the unit has come to function as a much better integrated team, it is possible to treat more disturbed girls successfully. As the stability increases, the patients and employees become more secure and it is now possible to support the periodically acutely disturbed girl. If morale and spirit of patients and employees are low, one explosive patient can light up the entire unit. On the other hand, if morale and atmosphere are unusually good, two or three disturbed patients can be handled with great therapeutic benefit within the unit itself.

One could almost put this down as an algebraic equation that the higher the esprit de corps in the unit, the great stress and strain it can successfully and therapeutically absorb. There is great therapeutic value in being able to maintain a girl in the unit through her acutely disturbed period rather than to transfer her out and have her return later.

Not only must the morale within the unit be a good one, but where a unit such as this is a small part of a much larger operation, there must be a smooth and harmonious relationship between the local administration of the Pavilion and the top administration of the hospital. There must be as much willingness to give and take on this level as on the lower levels. A feeling of frustration in the Director or Supervisor of the Pavilion cannot help but reflect itself within that small community. Each person in the unit must have a feeling of the worthwhileness of his particular job and appreciation of the overall goals of what he is doing. The top levels also must have the feeling of support from the highest levels that this work is being appreciated and warmly supported. Hence, the attitude of the Lay Board of Directors or of the community, which eventually supports the hospital, has an effect on the treatment program.

Other community relationships must be carefully considered in terms of the overall treatment design. A good relationship must be developed with outside agencies who may either refer cases or who may be able to assist in post-hospital planning for patients who have completed their treatment at the hospital. Thus, the therapeutic community becomes not only the hospital but any facility or agency in the community that can assist in the overall treatment design for any individual patient. We have had affiliations with the public high schools, the Linden Hill Cottage School, several child guidance agencies, various girls' clubs, foster homes for children and adolescents, courts, volunteer and fraternal organizations, general hospitals and state and private vocational rehabilitation and employment agencies.

DISCUSSION

The Pavilion was designed to be an intensive, individualized, psychoanalytically oriented treatment program in a group setting. While intensive psychotherapy is the core of treatment, it is the living group experience of the patient which makes this psychotherapy possible. The therapist is given an opportunity to understand and interpret, often for himself and not for the patient, what is going on within the patient by the multiple faceted images which he receives from the various adults working with the patient.

Simmel (1) explained that the patient's attitude in the hospital is merely a reflection of his behavior on the outside. The family situation is reenacted within the hospital structure—the patient playing the part he did in childhood. Simmel emphasized the extension of the doctor-patient relationship beyond the consulting room in attempting to comprehend many aspects of the patient's behavior. The in-patient is far more inclined than the out-patient to act out his conflicts.

Knight (2), one of the early psychiatrists to use analytic psychotherapy within a hospital, felt it vital to try and formulate a psychoanalytic understanding of the patient's behavior while under hospitalization.

Menninger (3) felt that the more training in psychoanalysis that was had by the psychiatrist and nursing staff, the better able they would be to administer to the unconscious needs of the patients as expressed in their symptoms and behavior. While this would be a most desirable situation, practically we are pleased to get mature, understanding personnel even though they may have had no experience whatever in psychoanalysis.

I would agree with Dr. Karl Menninger (4) who wrote, "We have not found it essential that a psychiatrist be analyzed in order to acquire such an attitude, i.e., an attitude which looks for unconscious motivation in the behavior of the patient." He believes that the proper attitude can be taught and furthermore that it is contagious. "It can be caught. Young psychiatrists quickly absorb the spirit and philosophy that permeates an institution."

Fromm-Reichmann (5) attached considerable importance to the psychotherapist joining in as part of the therapeutic community. She felt that he ought to participate in hospital activities even at the expense of his time with individual patients. He should make rounds, visit the occupational therapy shops and join in social functions. This alteration of role in the psychoanalyst is no doubt dictated by the type of patient treated at the hospital as well as the fact that the setting does not lend itself to an orthodox analytic technique.

The advice given by Chassel (6) seems most appropriate in dealing with our therapeutic community. He does not feel in dealing with psychotic or borderline patients that the usual psychoanalytic policy is really very helpful to the patient who has to fend for himself through the day apart from daily sessions with the analyst. The psychiatrist must accept that the patient unconsciously considers himself to be once again in the family scene and that the psychiatrist occupies the most important position in it. A completely passive attitude on the part of the psychiatrist is meaningless to the patient unless there is an opportunity to clarify fully for her the transference relationships, to distinguish that which is repetitive in the past from that which is present reality. Until such opportunities become available the doctor must realize that the patient looks to him for love, protection, restrictions, reprimands, advice and guidance, just as she has done throughout her life to those who are for her in "loco parentis."

The doctor is offered the opportunity in the Adolescent Pavilion to provide for the patients a healthy, living environment, to supply the girls with less destructive outlets than they had used prior to hospitalization and to supply desirable adult figures to whom the adolescents can relate and identify with. The role of the psychotherapist is to be able to coordinate these multiple functions and to dynamically understand the meaning of what is currently happening as a repetitive process in the patient's unconscious life. Whether he interprets this verbally to the patient or not would depend on therapeutic considerations.

CONCLUSION

We believe that the group setting of the Adolescent Pavilion at Hillside Hospital has made possible a type of individualized, psychoanalytically oriented psychotherapy that is frequently impossible with this type of acutely disturbed adolescent girl in conventional psychotherapy alone. Psychotherapy in this setting gives the doctor an opportunity to see in a living situation the patient's attempt to act out many of the previous family situations in childhood. It also gives the therapist an opportunity to create for the patient a more healthful, constructive environment which gives the patient in turn an opportunity to grow and to act in a more healthy way.

189

BIBLIOGRAPHY

1. Simmel, E.: Psychoanalytic treatment in a sanitorium. *Int. J. Psychoanal., 10:* 70, 1929.

2. Knight, R.: The relationship of psychoanalysis to psychiatry. *Am. J. Psychiat., 101:* 777, 1945.

3. Menninger, C.: Psychiatric hospital therapy designed to meet unconscious needs. *Am. J. Psychiat., 93:* 347, 1936.

4. Menninger, K. A.: Psychoanalytic psychiatry. Theory and practice. *Bull. Menninger Clinic, 4:* 105, 1940.

5. Fromm-Reichmann, F.: Problems of therapeutic management in a psychoanalytic hospital. *Psychoanalytic Quart., 16:* 325, 1947.

6. Chassel, J.: Psychoanalytic therapy in a mental hospital. *Psychiatry, 3:* 181, 1940.

STAFF ATTITUDES, DECISION-MAKING AND THE USE OF DRUG THERAPY IN THE MENTAL HOSPITAL

Gerald L. Klerman, M. D.

—

INTRODUCTION

It is generally acknowledged that the effectiveness of the tranquilizing drugs has induced significant secondary effects upon staff morale and hospital atmosphere (1-3). Through alleviation of over-activity, assaultiveness, incontinence and other forms of disturbed behavior, drug therapy has increased staff enthusiasm, reduced the use of seclusion and restraint, and produced indirect but measurable improvement in patients not on drug therapy (4). The widespread use of drug therapy in psychiatric hospitals has given impetus to the development of "open door" policies, higher discharge rates and community rehabilitation programs (5).

In this respect, the advent of tranquilizing drug therapy has coincided with growing recognition of the importance of social and milieu factors in treatment of psychiatric patients (6-7).

To a certain extent, it is unfortunate that these two currents in contemporary psychiatry—the advent of the new drugs, and discovery of the therapeutic potential of the milieu—should have made their impact in such close historical proximity. By emphasizing the important effects that drug therapy has had upon staff morale and hospital milieu, the impression is often conveyed that drug therapy alone has been responsible for the development of "open door" hospitals and recent increase in discharge rates. It seems important to reiterate that many of the major innovations in milieu therapy, both in Britain and in this country, began soon after World War II, at least 5-7 years before the introduction of chlorpromazine and reserpine.

The Massachusetts Mental Health Center has had extensive experience with the transition from a custodial organization to therapeutic community (8-9). The major results of these innovations had their impact before the advent of the new drugs; so that by 1954, when chlorpromazine and reserpine were first introduced into our hospital, significant progress had already been made toward the end of custodialism, intensification of treatment and increase in discharge rate (10).

193

In recent years, we have become interested in some of the relationships between psychiatric treatments and "milieu therapy." This paper will attempt to relate some of our experiences with the newer drug therapies to the growing body of knowledge about social processes within our hospital.

The major focus of the paper will be upon the divergent attitudes towards drug therapy held by different professional and staff groups. These attitudes are correlated with other features of the hospital social system and act as important influences upon decision-making.

THE SETTING:

A DESCRIPTION OF THE MASSACHUSETTS MENTAL HEALTH CENTER

The Massachusetts Mental Health Center is a small, intensive treatment state hospital with major teaching and research affiliations to Harvard Medical School. Its in-patient adult bed capacity at the time of these observations was 120 patients, a small Children's Service and an extensive out-patient department. The treatment of in-patients is carried on predominately by the psychiatric residents under the supervision of senior staff members. The number of residents assigned to the in-patient services averages between 12 and 16. The hospital is well staffed and is used as a training center by a number of medical, nursing, occupational therapy and social work schools in the Boston area. The admission rate varies between 800 and 900 patients a year, of whom approximately one-third are referred by the courts for diagnostic observation.

The hospital has been the object of extensive study by social scientists for almost a decade (11-15). Many aspects of its social structure and ward milieu are being evaluated and studied.

There is an active psychotherapy program based on a modified psychoanalytic model. Many members of the senior staff are

194

practicing psychoanalysts and members of the Boston Psychoanalytic Society. Training in psychodynamics and psychotherapy is a major focus of the medical student and residency programs (16). A high percentage of patients are treated with intensive psychotherapy; mostly by the residents. In addition, selected patients are seen for psychotherapy by psychologists and social workers.

Review of hospital records since 1952, indicates that approximately 45% of all admissions received some form of somatic therapy during this period. However, the type of treatment has changed over the past six years. ECT and Insulin Coma Therapy have been replaced in large part by the use of the newer drugs, and insulin coma was discontinued in the spring of 1958. Currently, 30-35% of all admissions receive drug therapy and 10-15% receive ECT at some time during their hospital stay.

THE SOMATIC THERAPY UNIT

The observations reported in this paper have been derived from over two years experience as a member of the Somatic Therapy Unit, which is responsible for the training of medical and non-medical staff, and supervision of patients receiving these therapies. The residents rotate through the Unit and assume partial responsibility for the prescription and application of different treatments.

As part of the Somatic Therapy Unit's activities, a weekly conference has been conducted at which time individual patients were reviewed in detail as to their history, psychodynamics and concurrent hospital activities. At the weekly case conferences, it was observed that the decision to employ drug therapy was intimately related to the dynamics of the doctor-patient relationship. This was especially evident in cases where the patient was also receiving individual psychotherapy. Further observations often revealed the close relationship of ward and hospital tensions to the referral of patients for somatic therapy.

195

INTERVIEWS AND PARTICIPANT OBSERVATION

To elaborate upon this clinical experience, interviews were conducted with members of the resident staff, and opinions and attitudes of medical staff towards the use of drugs and other somatic therapies were explored. Special focus was placed upon experience with drug therapy combined with psychotherapy. Informal interviews with members of various staff groups were also carried out to gather data on the attitudes and experiences of non-medical personnel.

Exploration of the context in which patients were referred for drug therapy revealed how frequently there were significant disagreements and tensions around the decision to employ drugs. Usually, the psychiatrist was the reluctant participant to chemotherapy, and was being urged to have his patient placed on drugs by a third party—the Ward Administrator, Chief of Service, the patient's relatives, the ward staff, or a senior hospital administrator.

An interesting paradox emerged. The psychiatrists having exclusive authority to prescribe drug therapy and possessing the greatest understanding of pharmacologic treatments, were the most reluctant to having a given patient treated with drugs. Regardless of other conflicts and disagreements among staff members as to the treatment and management of the individual patient, referral for drug therapy was itself a decision about which staff members disagreed.

Survey of members of various staff groups, psychiatrists, nurses, psychologists, attendants, social workers, student groups, clerical and housekeeping workers, revealed the existence of marked differences of opinion about the indications for drug therapy and the value and effectiveness of this form of treatment.

This paper will focus upon the significance of the different attitudes towards drug therapy held by professional and staff groups within the hospital. This should not be taken as implying that these divergent attitudes were the only sources of staff disagree-

196

ment, nor even the major source. Indeed, the divergence of opinions and disagreements over referring patients for drug therapy was often only a manifest issue masking other latent conflicts and disagreements. However, it is the central thesis of this paper that the attitudes of staff groups towards the use of drugs are important influences in the psychiatrists' prescription of drugs.

OBSERVATIONS AND FINDINGS

Staff Attitudes Towards Drug Therapy

The various staff groups in the hospital were found to hold significantly different attitudes towards drug treatment. Table I outlines the dominant, or usual, attitude of the occupational group. It is recognized that within each group certain individuals may hold variant attitudes. This is most marked among the psychiatrists.

TABLE I

CONTINUUM OF ATTITUDES HELD BY DIFFERENT
STAFF GROUPS TOWARDS USE OF DRUG THERAPY

Staff Group	Dominant Attitude	Remarks
Psychiatrists	+ —	Sharp Split and Ambivalence Within Medical Staff
Psychologists	—	
Social Workers	—	
Occupational Therapy	+ —	Side-effects Limit Activities
Professional Nurses	+ +	
Ward Staff	+ + +	Attendants, Student Nurses, Aides
Service Personnel	+ + +	Kitchen Staff, Housekeeping and Clerical Personnel

The medical staff was found to occupy a significant position in this attitude continuum. They were for the most part ambivalent

197

in their attitudes towards the value and effectiveness of drug treatment. In general, the more junior members of the medical staff were found to be resistant to drug therapy. The more senior members of the medical staff, especially those concerned with hospital administration, were more directly aware of the patient's manifest behavior and sensitive to the hospital's need to maintain tension at a low level. They were usually less reluctant to refer patients for drug therapy. Frequently the referral was initiated by one of the senior administrative persons or by the ward administrator.

The members of staff groups in positions of lower status and less authority than the physicians were found to hold increasingly positive attitudes towards somatic therapy. Ward staff, attendants and practical nurses held, for the most part, a positive attitude towards drugs. Chlorpromazine was even referred to as "the nurses' friend." The enthusiasm of nursing and ward staff towards drug therapy was of the most commented upon features of drug therapy. Because the attendants and nursing personnel had direct contact with patients' manifest behavior, they looked to drug therapy as a means of controlling disturbed and anti-social behavior when their own efforts had failed.

The social workers and psychologists were found to hold a different position. They had little training or knowledge about physiology or drugs. They had been trained and skilled in verbal techniques for communication and treatment. Seeing patients at selected times and usually only for scheduled appointments, they were found to be less concerned with manifest and disturbed behavior than the ward staff who were in direct contact with patients.

Relationship of Attitude Towards Drug Therapy and Commitment to Psychotherapy

An inverse relationship between the degree of enthusiasm for drug therapy and the corresponding attitude towards psychotherapy was found. More positive attitudes towards psychotherapy were frequently to be found among those with the greatest degree of reluctance towards the use of somatic therapy.

Psychiatrists treating a patient with psychotherapy were usually reluctant to add drug therapy. Because of this fact, the Somatic Therapy Unit grew suspicious when a resident had referred a patient for drug therapy whom he had been seeing regularly in psychotherapy. The rationale usually offered that "psychotherapy had failed" frequently masked an unresolved countertransference. The resident's psychotherapy supervisor would take issue with this referral and bring his knowledge of the countertransference problem to bear upon the decision.

More frequent, however, the referral for drug therapy came not from the resident but from the ward administrator. The reason for referral was usually disturbed behavior or some unrecognized impasse in the psychotherapy. Because this impasse was manifested by an aggravation of the patient's behavior, the ward administrator would pressure the resident to deal with the symptoms (22).

The ward administrator or chief of service, being the responsible physician, functioned as the mediator and arbitrator of these conflicts. As a psychiatrist having been a junior resident and usually committed to psychotherapy, the young administrator experienced a conflict of loyalties and values. He usually was cognizant and appreciative of the analytic problems, but felt there was insufficient time to work them through. Or, as was more often the case, he decided that the needs of the ward as a whole could not tolerate the time and effort required.

In general, the younger members of the medical staff, especially the residents, were found to be committed in almost an idealistic way to belief in the value and effectiveness of psychotherapy, and were reluctant to refer patients for any somatic therapy. When they did so, or were urged to do so by others, it was with a sense of guilt and misgiving.

199

\The advent of drug therapy highlighted the ambiguities in the psychiatrist's professional status as a medical person./ On one hand, by prescribing drugs, he came closer in role performance to his medical colleagues. But, drug therapy blurred the uniqueness of psychotherapy and was seen by many psychiatrists as in conflict with their psychotherapist role.

The junior residents, social workers and psychologists were the hospital groups best trained for and most involved in psychotherapy. Many members of these groups were in personal psychoanalysis for professional as well as therapeutic goals. In general, they were accustomed to verbal and intellectual contacts with patients and throughout their own social life. Social workers and psychologists, interested as they are in the psychoanalytic model of treatment, see drug therapy as a potential threat in their attempts to achieve equality with the psychiatrist.

Nursing, attendant and occupational therapy staff people usually know little about psychotherapy, and have a fair amount of misapprehension about psychoanalytic concepts. In recent years these barriers have been broken down as part of the in-service training policy of the hospital and there has been an increasing interest on the part of all staff persons in psychodynamic psychiatry.

Attitude Towards Drug Therapy and Occupational Role

What were the role correlates to these attitudes? Table II shows a correlation between attitudes held towards somatic therapy and the type of relationship between staff person and patient.

It was noted that members of the ward staff, attendants and nurses, were involved in on-going, continuous and face-to-face relationships with the patients. Their concerns for the patient were in terms of specific and concrete behavioral matters; i.e., eating, dress, cleanliness, ward activities.

This was in contrast to the relatedness of social workers, psychiatrists and psychologists. They saw patients for discontinuous

TABLE II

CORRELATES OF ATTITUDES TOWARDS DRUG THERAPY

Staff Group	Attitude Towards Drug Therapy	Psychotherapy Commitment	Type of Patient-Staff Relationship	Degree of Tolerance of Disturbed Behavior
Psychiatrists Psychologists Social Workers	Ambivalent or Negative	Strong-Active Participants in Psychotherapy	Scheduled Discontinuous Predominantly Verbal	High
Professional Nurses Occupational Therapists	Varies	Growing with Professionalization of Group	Highly Variable	Moderately High
Nurses Attendants Ward Staff	Strongly Positive	Weak—Not Active Participants in Psychotherapy	Continuous Face-to-Face Concrete Activities	Varies

periods, usually at formally scheduled appointments—"the hour." During these appointments they would be mainly concerned with the patients' verbal behavior. As such, they were not directly involved in the manifest or symptomatic behavior of the patients in the ward setting.

Problems that patients presented here, such as eating, sleeping, dress, noisiness, were rarely observed directly by the medical staff. They came to their attention only as a result of communication from the nursing and ward personnel.

Another important correlate of attitudes to drugs was found to be the staff persons varying degrees of tolerance of deviant and disturbed behavior. The medical, social work and psychology staff, in general, were found to hold a permissive and tolerant attitude towards disturbed behavior. This was considered one of the characteristics of the modern trend in psychiatry. Permissiveness was regarded by others as a luxury that could only be held by people who were not in direct contact with patients when they were upset. Doctors, social workers and psychologists had the prerogative to leave the ward, contrary to the nursing and ward staff who were there for eight hour periods. The latter groups held a lower tolerance towards disturbed behavior and were found to be less permissive.

DISCUSSION

Consensus and Disagreement in Decision-Making Process

The nursing and ward staff are in the setting where they are directly involved in the manifest behavior of patients. However, they do not have the authority to prescribe those forms of treatment which, in their mind, are the most directly effective in the control of deviant behavior. In order to have a patient placed on chlorpromazine, ECT or other somatic therapy, it was necessary for the ward staff to communicate their desire either directly or indirectly to the medical staff.

The request could be made directly by nurse or attendant, suggesting clearly to the doctor that a given patient should receive a

202

given form of treatment. More frequently, this came through indirect communication. Usually it was by informing the doctor of the patient's behavior at the "morning report." The doctor then had to evaluate the nature of the information and also to perceive the implicit request for assistance that frequently accompanied these reports of disturbed behavior. This created an interesting paradox; the people who were most involved with patient behavior were the ones who were not in authority to prescribe somatic therapy. They were dependent upon the authority of the medical staff.

The daily situation in which these different attitudes were most apparent was at the "morning report." The hospital was, at that time, divided into two active treatment services, each consisting of two wards, and each led by a chief of service who was the administrator and coordinator of the staff on the service. The staff met together with its chief of service each morning. At this time, the chief nurse on the ward would report to the assembled group of doctors, social workers, psychologists, occupational therapists and attendants on the behavior of patients during the preceding day.

The ward nurse was at this meeting in a strategic position. By reporting to the medical staff, she was in a position to influence treatment and management through the nature and quality of this information. Patients whom the nursing staff felt they could control were less likely to be brought up as ward problems. If the behavior persisted over a number of days, the patient then became a "management problem," and communication from the nurse at report was expressed in terms which made more and more explicit a demand for the use of somatic treatment.

The nursing group was found to be in an interesting position; it is the professional group in marginal status. In recent years, there had been a growing trend towards the professionalization of nursing. Increasing numbers were obtaining collegiate and graduate degrees. As this occurred, there was an increasing prestige placed upon higher education, research and psychodynamic understanding of patients. At our hospital, numbers of the nursing group have gained experience in intensive nursing relationships with patients modeled on the psychotherapeutic relationship (18). As this developed, some nurses tended to adopt the attitudes of the junior medical staff and came to share some of their reluctance for the use of drugs. Their interest now centers around developing nursing and interpersonal skills for the management of difficult patients.

The medical staff had come to rely upon the ward staff for the day-to-day management of patient needs. It also depended upon the staff reports and communications as the bases to make decisions. While the medical staff had the formal power to decide patients' care, this was dependent at all points upon the consensus and cooperation of the ward staff.

In general, there was found to be an implicit contract between the ancillary personnel and the medical staff. The ward staff would, in general, maintain agreement with the program of the medical staff so long as the degree of patient manifest disturbed behavior was not threatening.

In practice this meant that the members of the ward staff would tolerate a fair amount of disturbed and deviant behavior when their morale was high and their rapport with the medical staff was good.

The medical staff is divided in its attitudes towards drugs. This division represents one of the most striking features of American psychiatry (19, 20). The decision to use drugs depends not only upon the attitudes of the psychiatrists but also upon the needs of the ward and the capacity of the ward staff to tolerate and deal with patients' behavior. In general, hospitals with well-developed programs of psychotherapy have different attitudes towards drug therapy than do the larger state hospitals (21, 22).

DRUG THERAPY AND THE THERAPEUTIC COMMUNITY

Drug therapy is particularly effective for patients with manifest disturbed behavior and the rate of prescription depends often on the general level of ward tension. When the ward group is more disturbed, or there is poor morale or high tension among the ward staff, the use of drugs is greater.) At such times, there is generally less tolerance of disturbed behavior. This phenomena has been described and documented by Sabshin (23). The latent conflict underlying this situation may be within the patient group or within the ward staff. In this situation, the referral for drug treatment is motivated by the need to reduce the general level of ward tension.

However, at other times, the situation is less clear. Sometimes the source of strain is open and overt, such as the change of charge nurse or recent increase in number of admissions, or open personality clash between staff persons. In situations manifested by tension and disturbance within a single patient, a group of patients, or the ward as a whole, the ward administrator is often hard pressed to ascertain the source of strain. The most difficult situations to diagnose are the forms of covert disagreement, what have come to be called "Stanton-Schwartz Phenomena." In their now classic book, *The Mental Hospital* (24), the authors put forward the thesis that the disturbed behavior of patients was often related to the presence of covert conflict between two or more members of the staff involved in the care of the patient. It has been our observation that patients are often referred for somatic treatment because of the development of disturbed behavior which is perpetuated in spite of active psychotherapeutic intervention. Investigation frequently reveals that this continued disturbed behavior occurs in the context of covert staff disagreement. The patient is then referred for the treatment of manifest behavior without awareness that this is related to significant but covert staff conflict.

The concept of "A Therapeutic Community" has many meanings and components. Prominent in the literature is the emphasis upon communication and the importance of the resolution of conflict and strain by participation of all parties concerned.

It is unclear to what extent the strains outlined in this paper are unique to a "therapeutic community." There is evidence that they may be dormant and latent in more traditional hospital structures (25) and become open, and hopefully, more easily resolved in the transition to "therapeutic community (26)."

In this respect, the shift from custodial orientation in the mental hospital to a "therapeutic community" orientation involved a democratization of the hospital power structure and the development of equalitarian trends in staff relations. In this process, the power and authority structure changes and each staff group becomes more nearly a "veto group" limiting the formal authority of other groups (27). Another important feature of "therapeutic community," and one which has gained significance from the experience of the British, is the emphasis on "The Open Hospital" and the trend away from custodial attitudes and restrictive practices.

These attitudes are based on many factors, including the social background and education of members of staff groups. As Levinson and Gilbert have shown, "custodialism," as an attitude towards mental illness, is highest among the ward and service personnel (28). One of the most important tasks in establishing a therapeutic milieu is the education of ward and nursing staff in the principles of non-restraint and changing their attitude from custodialism to active participation with patients.

It is sometimes claimed that the pressure for drug therapy arose out of the need for the control of manifest disturbed behavior in order to maintain the hospital's commitment of an "open door" policy. According to this viewpoint, an open door policy with general permissiveness means that some form of chemical or somatic treatment restraint is necessary in order to substitute for physical restraint or the restraint of locked doors. However, it is uncertain whether or not the open door policy means an increase in use of drugs. There is evidence from certain centers that the need for ECT and sedation decreases after "open door" program (29). Further research, perhaps comparing different types of hospitals, will be required to answer this important question.

SUMMARY AND CONCLUSIONS

Recent pharmacological advances have provided psychiatric hospitals with powerful agents for modifying disturbed and deviant patient behavior. Although agreement as to the efficacy and utility of these drugs is growing, there are still situations and areas where there is disagreement and uncertainty. This is especially evident in institutions where psychotherapy and milieu therapy are most intensively developed.

The decision to employ drug therapy involves a complex interaction between patient, psychiatrist, hospital staff and family. Frequently the use of drugs occurs in the context of significant disagreement. One of the sources of disagreement lies in the differential attitudes held by staff members as to the indications for, and effectiveness of drug therapy.

Observations have been presented to demonstrate the continuum of attitudes towards drug therapy held by staff groups. The correlates of these attitudes involve significant aspects of occupational role, idealogy and social functioning. Further systematic investigation will be necessary to verify these findings.

Implicit in this paper's approach is the concept that decision-making in the psychiatric hospital involves the interplay of attitudes, ideologies, occupational status, and formal and informal power. Further research will be required to elucidate these forces.

Decision-making in drug therapy can thus be viewed in a larger framework of the hospital as a social, cultural and political system.

ACKNOWLEDGMENT

Acknowledgment is offered to my colleagues in this endeavor, many of whose ideas are embodied in this paper; Lester L. Havens, M. D.; Robert Moore, M. D.; Dexter Bullard, Jr., M. D.; Edward Brennan, M. D.; Ralph Colp, Jr., M. D.; William Carmichael, M. D. and George Perrin, M. D.

BIBLIOGRAPHY

1. Freyhan, F. A.: The immediate and long range effects of chlorpromazine on the mental hospital. In: *Chlorpromazine and Mental Health,* Philadelphia, Lea and Febiger, 1955.

2. Pollack, B.: Drug therapy — clinical and operational effects: changes in the mental hospital resulting from the addition of chlorpromazine to the total therapeutic program. *Mental Hospitals, 7:* 14, 1957.

3. Linn, E. L.: Drug therapy, milieu change and release from a mental hospital. *A.M.A. Arch. Neurol. Psychiat.* In press.

4. Meszaros, A. F.: Factors influencing indirect effect of tranquilizing drugs. In: Sarwer-Foner, G. (ed.) *The Dynamics of Psychiatric Drug Therapy.* Springfield, Thomas, 1959. In press.

5. Brill, H., and Patton, R. E.: Analysis of the 1955-1956 population fall in New York state mental hospitals. *Am. J. Psychiat., 144:* 509, 1957.

6. Rioch, D. McK., and Stanton, A. H.: Milieu therapy. *Psychiatric Treatment,* Vol. 21. A.R.N.M.D. Baltimore, Williams and Wilkins, 1953.

7. Jones, M.: *The Therapeutic Community.* New York, Basic Books, 1953.

8. Hyde, R. W., and Solomon, H. C.: Clinical management of psychiatric hospitals. *Conn. S. Med., 15:* 301, 1951.

9. Hyde, R. W.: *Experiencing the Patients Day.* New York, G. P. Putnam Sons, 1955.

10. Greenblatt, M., York, R., and Brown, E. L.: *From Custodial to Therapeutic Care in Mental Hospitals.* New York, Russell Sage Foundation, 1955.

11. Barrabee, P. S.: *A Study of a Mental Hospital.* Unpublished Ph.D. Thesis, Department of Social Relations, Harvard University, 1951.

12. Boyd, R. W., Kegeles, F. S., and Greenblatt, M.: Outbreak of gang destructive behavior in a psychiatric ward. *J. Nerv. Ment. Dis., 120:* 338, 1954.

13. Greenblatt, M., Levinson, D. L., and Williams, R. W.: *The Patient and the Mental Hospital.* Glencoe, The Free Press, 1957.

14. Landy, D.: The anthropologist and the mental hospital. *Human Organization, 17:* 30, 1959.

15. Gallagher, E., Levinson, D. L., and Erlich, I.: Some sociopsychological characteristics of patients and their relevance for psychiatric treatment. In: Greenblatt, Levinson and Williams, *op. cit.*

16. Sharaf, M. R., and Levinson, D. L.: Patterns of ideology and role definition among psychiatric residents. In: Greenblatt, Levinson and Williams, *op. cit.*

17. Klerman, G. L.: Unpublished data.

18. Mellow, J.: Research in psychiatric nursing; two nursing therapies with individual patients. *Am. J. Nursing, 55:* 572, 1955.

19. Feldman, P. E.: The personal element in psychiatric research. *Am. J. Psychiat., 113:* 52, 1956.

20. MacIver, J., and Redlich, F. C.: Patterns of psychiatric practice. *Am. J. Psychiat., 115:* 692, 1959.

21. Donnelly, J., and Zeller, W.: Clinical research on chlorpromazine and reserpine in state and private psychiatric hospitals. *J. of Clin. and Exper. Psychopath. and Quart. Rev. Psychiat. and Neurol., 17:* 180, 1956.

22. Sabshin, M., and Ramot, J.: Pharmacotherapeutic evaluation and the psychiatric setting. *A.M.A. Arch. Neurol. Psychiat., 75:* 362, 1956.

23. Sabshin, M., and Eisen, S. B.: The effects of ward tension on the quality and quantity of tranquilizer utilization. *Ann. New York Acad. Sci., 67:* 746, 1957.

24. Stanton, A. H., and Schwartz, M. S.: *The Mental Hospital.* New York, Basic Books, 1954.

25. Cummings, E., and Cummings, J.: The locus of power in a large mental hospital. *Psychiatry, 19:* 361, 1956.

26. Rapaport, R. N., and Rapaport, R.: Democratization and authority in a therapeutic community. *Behavioral Science, 2:* 128, 1957.

27. Reisman, D., Glazer, N., and Denny, R.: *The Lonely Crowd.* New Haven, Yale University Press, 1950.

28. Gilbert, D. C., and Levinson, D. L.: Ideology, personality and institutional policy in the mental hospital. *J. Abnor. and Soc. Psychiat.*, 53: 363, 1953.

29. Stanton, A. H.: *Problems in Analysis of Therapeutic Implications of the Institutional Milieu.* In: Symposium on Preventive and Social Psychiatry, Washington, D. C., Walter Reed Army Institute of Research, 1957.

DISCUSSION OF DR. KLERMAN'S PAPER

DR. MAX POLLACK:—

I should like Dr. Klerman to comment on one aspect of decision-making that was not stressed in his presentation. Namely, the relation of the social status of both patient and staff toward somatotherapy. In the table shown, there appears to be a correlation between staff hierarchy and attitude toward drug therapy. The psychiatrist, social worker and psychologist who come from the upper classes have a negative attitude toward drugs, while the nurses and ward personnel who may come from lower social classes have a positive attitude. Is it possible that the psychiatrist's ambivalent attitude toward drugs is not a general one but is related to the "social distance" of the patient? We have found in our studies at Hillside Hospital that both referral for, and acceptance of somatotherapy, is influenced by the patient's social class. Perhaps the psychiatric resident has no qualms about administering drugs to a lower class patient, but is indecisive when it comes to recommending drugs for a patient who is culturally more like himself.

REPLY BY DR. KLERMAN:—

The questions raised by Dr. Pollack have to do with the relationships between the social class of the psychiatrist and the psychiatrists' attitudes towards the use of drug therapy.

I would agree with Dr. Pollack's observation that "psychiatrists, social workers, and psychologists, who come from the upper classes have a negative attitude towards drugs, while the nurses and ward personnel who may come from lower social classes have a positive attitude." It would seem that there is a correspondence between the social status of various occupational groups and their attitude towards psychiatric therapies. A number of studies, including the work of Redlich and Hollingshead at Yale, have substantiated the relationship between social class membership and attitudes towards various psychiatric treatments. It seems reasonable to conclude from the available evidence that members of the upper social classes are more oriented towards verbal communication and psychotherapy than members of working class groups. Members of working class groups tend to see psychiatric treatment more in terms of standard relationship to medical persons as authorities and look to psychiatric treatment in terms of medication or other physical treatments. The social system of the hospital corresponds in these respects to the larger community.

The psychiatrists' attitude towards psychotherapy and somatic therapy is thus in line with his general middle class and upper middle class membership. However, there is a conflict between the values which he holds as a psychiatrist and those attitudes towards treatment with which he was inculcated during his medical school and internship training. Throughout most of medicine, the predominant theory of disease involves the concept of causation and organ pathology. The treatment of disease in this view is seen as the removal of some form of pathology by surgery, medication or other physiological treatment. The psychiatrist's attitude in this respect is deviant from the rest of the medical profession. This creates a conflict within the psychiatrist between his previous learned values as a physician and his new values in psychotherapy. The extent to which this conflict operates in his day to day functioning as a clinician are yet to be fully investigated.

Dr. Pollack further raises the possibility that the psychiatrist's ambivalence towards the prescription of drugs is not necessarily a general one, and the ambivalence towards drugs is less when there is a greater degree of social distance between the patient and the psychiatrist. This hypothesis would imply that the closer the patient and the psychiatrist are to each other in social class membership, the less will be the psychiatrist's inclination to prescribe drugs, ECT or other somatic therapies. Conversely, the psychiatrist would be less hesitant about prescribing drugs to patients who are members of social classes or ethnic groups other than his own. These seem to me to be reasonable hypotheses and are capable of being tested in almost any clinic setting. My impression would be that the data would substantiate these hypotheses. However, I have no observations directly bearing on these interesting points that Dr. Pollack raises.

In conclusion, I would like to offer the suggestion that the underlying process involved in these phenomena is not so much the social class one, but rather has to do with more personal value orientations. It seems to me that psychiatrists, psychologists, and social workers are members of a unique professional and social group whose primary value centers around the efficacy and faith of psychotherapy. It seems that there is more involved in this cluster of values than just the orientation towards psychotherapy as a form of treatment for mental illness; the reliance on psychotherapy seems to correspond to a whole series of values about the importance of rationality, certain attitudes towards authority, and points of view towards important social issues. The work of Levinson and his associates in Boston, Redlich and MacIver at Yale, Deasy and Schaffer at Bethesda, all are in line with the observation that the psychiatrist who is positively oriented towards psychotherapy is also the one who shares with his colleagues certain aspects of a larger world view and specific orientations to certain social and cultural problems. Further research is needed to specify social characteristics and values of this professional group and to demonstrate their relationship to such important variables as social and religious background, patterns of psychiatric practice, including the prescription of drugs and of electric shock therapy.

What we seem to be arriving at are the outlines of a social psychology of the psychiatrist, a field which may become as important in our understanding of mental illness as the psychology of the patient.

212

DISCUSSION OF DR. KLERMAN'S PAPER

DR. MAX FINK:—

For the past half-year two of the psychiatrists at Hillside, Drs. A. Kaplen and H. Lefkowits, have been studying the problem of why patients are referred for somatic therapies. In addition to Dr. Klerman's suggestion of impasse on the ward and staff disagreement as being basic in such referrals, these investigators have found a number of other factors operating in our institution. First, the referrals appear during two periods of the patient's hospitalization. There are a group of patients who were referred early in hospitalization, that is within the first month. In such, it is quite obvious that behavioral manifestations predominate and are probably the instrumental element in referral. Such patients are excited, assaultive, depressed and withdrawn, or in a variety of ways are in such states that psychotherapy, which is the primary treatment mode, is not readily possible. But there are another group of referrals. These are patients who have been in the institution for four to eight months. In such patients, behavioral manifestations are not overtly different than what had probably been prominent for a good many months before. In discussing the reasons for referral Drs. Kaplen and Lefkowits observed that about one-third of the patients were referred because of a "failure in psychotherapy" or "to enhance psychotherapy." We interpret this as a manifestation of the therapist's frustration. A few patients have been referred because of administrative demands. There is, at Hillside Hospital, a general feeling that patients will not be kept beyond a year. A patient who has shown little response to hospitalization by the eighth or ninth month is often considered for alternate treatments with the awareness that discharge from the institution is imminent and perhaps more behavioral change could be developed using alternate methods.

There are another series of studies at Hillside which are relevant to Dr. Klerman's paper. Drs. Kahn and Pollack have been studying various aspects of the psychology of patients and relating these to the choice of treatment, diagnoses, duration of hospitalization and results of treatment. They have made some interest-

213

ing observations. For example, in our population those patients who are older, less educated, foreign born and with high scores on the California F scale as modified by Dan Levinson, are those who are referred for convulsive therapy early in hospitalization, respond best to such treatment, and whose total hospital course is shorter than patients receiving other treatments. Patients who are young, highly educated, American born and with scores on the F scale that are low are generally not referred for convulsive or drug therapies. These patients are maintained in psychotherapy and there is a linear relationship between these factors and the duration of hospitalization. Such patients, if referred for drug therapy, are referred late in their course. It is the contention of Drs. Kahn and Pollack that therapists maintain patients in psychotherapy in direct proportion to the similarity in background of the patient with that of the therapist. They are now involved in further amplification of these observations, specifically with attempts at demonstrating the significance of communication patterns in these observations.

DISCUSSION OF DR. KLERMAN'S PAPER

DR. A. F. MESZAROS:—

Motivations in the choice of treatment have been exemplarily analyzed in this paper. The study points to the importance of selective attitudes by which treatment methods are accepted, esteemed or rejected by the staff. The staff attitude concerning a treatment method might be regarded as a significant factor in the total treatment situation. Staff attitude to a particular form of treatment and the choice of treatment for a particular patient might be the condensed expression of the interpersonal forces which surround the patient in the hospital milieu. Thus, the emotional background of decision, agreement and disagreement probably have an influence on the result of treatment.

FACTORS INFLUENCING THE DISCHARGE OF CHRONIC SCHIZOPHRENIC PATIENTS

Dexter M. Bullard, Jr., M. D.,
and
Barbara R. Hoffman, A. B.

215

In practice, the therapeutic community must include concern for the problem of chronic schizophrenia, since these patients constitute the largest single group remaining in mental hospitals. The present report will discuss some of the factors influencing the discharge of chronic schizophrenic patients.

The material is derived from a research project comparing the effectiveness of tranquilizing drugs in different hospital populations. As one part of the study, two groups of chronic schizophrenic patients, totaling 46, were compared. They were selected from the patient population of Metropolitan State Hospital in Waltham, Massachusetts, and chosen primarily on the basis of their chronicity. Hospitalization had been continuous for at least five years, and the average length of stay was 11.7 years. The ages ranged from 25 to 50 years, with an average of 38 years.

Twenty-two patients remained in their original setting. Twenty-four (14 females and 10 males) selected randomly were transferred to the Massachusetts Mental Health Center, a 120-bed research and teaching center in the state hospital system of the Commonwealth of Massachusetts.

Both groups received drug therapy with chlorpromazine, reserpine, and trihexiphenidyl for a six month period (1)*. Those remaining at the state hospital received whatever social therapy was available to long-term patients on their custodial ward. The others were transferred for intensive treatment, using the more extensive facilities and staff of the smaller hospital.

Since we had made no attempt to select patients in terms of their clinical condition, there were many degrees of disability within the group. The patients varied from being totally immobilized to maintaining a self-sufficient and productive role within the hospital. Nevertheless, even the best adjusted patients showed many evidences of disability, including a marked incapacity to form relationships and deterioration in their ability to care for

---

* Dr. George Brooks of the Vermont State Hospital developed the dosage regimen and initiated this project during six months spent at the Massachusetts Mental Health Center for research (1).

themselves. They were without initiative or apparent interest in their future, withdrawn, isolated and apathetic.

The patients were transferred to the Massachusetts Mental Health Center at the rate of one a week. On arrival, drugs were started and each patient was assigned to a resident and social worker. Auxiliary services of the hospital, such as occupational and physical therapy, etc., were mobilized to work as intensively as possible with this group. Each patient remained for six months unless discharged earlier. At the end of this time, he was returned to his original hospital unless discharge was imminent; in two cases patients were kept on somewhat longer than six months, but in no instance longer than nine months.

Throughout this report we use the word "discharge" to mean discharge from full in-patient status. In all cases, the hospital remained responsible for some aspect of the patient's life and all the patients rated as "discharged" retained some disability.

At the end of the six month period, five patients had been on a disturbed ward for the entire time and three others made only minimal or brief adjustments to open wards. Improvement was shown in a number of these cases but none sufficiently to be considered for discharge.

Sixteen patients were considered for discharge at one time or another during their stay. They were on open wards at their original hospital or rapidly moved to the convalescent wards at the Massachusetts Mental Health Center. They initially showed the least evidence of psychosis, or improved sufficiently to merit discharge planning. Some held jobs in hospital industry. They were all able to communicate realistically on a limited basis, to care for themselves without assistance from ward personnel, and were not bizarre in their daily behavior.

Eight of these 16 "better" patients were discharged, comprising one-third of the total group. Although the discharges came from the "better" group, these patients had not succeeded in getting out of the their original hospital and none were being considered for discharge at the time of their transfer.

To ascertain the factors distinguishing the discharged from the non-discharged patients, we first studied the mental status and social behavior of the 16 "better" patients. The patients were evaluated by two methods. One consisted of interviews and mental status examinations by a psychiatrist and observation of the patient's ward behavior by a social psychologist. A second assessment was made using two rating scales administered to ward personnel—the Barabee-Hyde Social Adjustment Scale and the Bedford Clinical Rating Scale. Comparing the eight patients who had been discharged with the eight remaining hospitalized, we could find no differences. Non-discharged patients often showed fewer disabling symptoms and more social facility than those discharged. In addition, both groups showed approximately equal improvement over the six month period.

Having found no essential differences in the clinical condition of those patients discharged and those not, we examined the interaction of the patient with the hospital milieu and the nature of the treatment given each patient. The one uniform treatment regimen given was a combination of tranquilizing drugs. Beyond this, the treatment program for each patient varied markedly. No attempt was made to control the hospital milieu to offer each patient identical treatment since this was neither clinically indicated nor feasible. Therefore, some patients made more use of hospital facilities than others. Some participated in occupational therapy, physical therapy, the industrial and rehabilitation programs, some concentrated on one area of hospital activity, while others remained almost completely uninvolved. We studied the relationship between participation in the various areas of hospital milieu and discharge. The degree of involvement in the milieu did not prove to be related to discharge. In short, it did not matter how much the patient participated in activities insofar as his getting out of the hospital was concerned.

One correlation between treatment and discharge did occur. Each patient was assigned a doctor and a social worker at the time of transfer to the Massachusetts Mental Health Center. We found marked differences in the amount of contact the doctors and social workers had with their patients. Some saw their patients in regularly scheduled interviews throughout the six month period. The contacts between the other doctors and social workers and their patients varied widely. In some cases psychotherapy or social casework was begun but terminated; some doctors and social workers saw their patients briefly on the ward for varying amounts of time, while others saw their patients only when some problem arose or to assist the patients in such things as job hunting or purchasing clothes.

We found no correlation between unscheduled contacts with the patients and discharge. There was, however, a statistically significant relationship between regularly scheduled interviews and discharge. Eight patients were seen by a doctor or social worker at least one hour a week in an office setting for the six month period. Six of these eight patients were discharged, while only 2 of the 16 patients who did not receive psychotherapy or social casework therapy were able to leave the hospital. The orientation of this treatment varied from case to case, according to the patient's disability and the person doing the therapy. Although we will use the term "psychotherapy" or "social casework" to describe them, the interviews ranged from a largely supportive relationship to insight psychotherapy.

Why did some patients receive this particular form of therapy while others did not? Severity of illness played a part in the selection of patients for treatment. None of the eight patients unable to make a successful open ward adjustment received this treatment. Limiting ourselves to the 16 patients who could adjust to the open wards, however, we could find no features which distinguished those selected for psychotherapy or social casework. The proportion of males and females treated was the same. Their cases did not appear more hopeful or amenable to treatment. Other studies have indicated that a doctor's choice of patients for therapy is often determined by subtle aspects of the patient's character but, in this instance, we found other factors to be of more importance.

In our study, particular doctors rather than particular patients were the determining factors in the use of psychotherapy for treatment. The doctors assigned to these patients were 15 first and second year psychiatric residents in the hospital. None of the seven second year residents undertook this form of treatment with their patients. Only three of the eight first year residents continued their patients in psychotherapy or assigned them to social workers for casework for the six month period. Two of the three treated their patients themselves in weekly or twice weekly interviews. The third resident continued management of his cases but supervised weekly interviews between his patients and social workers. All three residents had some particular interest in chronic mental illness.

There were several reasons why the remaining doctors did not use this form of treatment. The hospital is normally oriented to short term acute illness and the interest of many first year residents centers upon such cases. The second year residents are more limited in time and receive experience with chronic illness at a large state hospital. Most of them felt that psychotherapy would be ineffectual and not worth their time.

Treating the patient with psychotherapy was not the only factor correlated with discharge. A significantly larger number of women were discharged, seven out of eight. Two male patients who received psychotherapy were not discharged and two female patients were discharged without it. All four patients were well adjusted to convalescent wards and, in the opinion of the staff, could live outside the hospital in a protected environment. The families of the male patients were unable or unwilling to accept them, while female family placement was successful.

These latter four cases demonstrated to us that in addition to the patient's clinical state and treatment, the family situation is of prime importance in discharge planning for chronic patients. Many of our patients no longer required hospitaliaztion for psychiatric reasons, although they retained some disability. The major barrier to discharge in these cases was finding a suitable place for the patient to live since most needed a protective environment at least temporarily. The placement most readily available for them was with their families. Five of the eight patients discharged went directly to live with relatives. Three patients who could not be placed with their families went to one or another form of protective environment. One went to the hospital's halfway house, one took a job as a mother's helper and the third obtained a live-in job in a nursing home. This latter patient is the only one who has relapsed and remained hospitalized. The patient who worked as a mother's helper held the job only three months and then went to live with relatives. Thus, within three months after discharge, the only patient not living with his family was the one in the hospital's half-way house. Our experiences point up the difficulties encountered in placing patients outside their families and illustrate why the hospital failed to discharge eight patients who had made successful hospital adjustments. The families of six of these patients were either unable to support additional members at home or unwilling to take the patient unless he was completely cured. All were returned to their original hospital. Two others could not be discharged for other reasons.

Five of the six patients whose families could not or would not take them were men. This failure to discharge male patients to their families contrasts with the greater success in discharging women. Apparently, families of female patients are more willing to accept them. Family members expressed fears of the possible aggressive actions of male patients, but did not seem to have such fears about female patients. Furthermore, family expectations of performance in female patients appeared to be less. Since the patients were generally unemployable at discharge, we speculate that families are less likely to require female members to hold jobs.

Placing the patient in the community is not the end of the story. In all our cases we found that continued effort was required to maintain the patient outside the hospital. After discharge, the hospital remained an important factor in the patient's life. Our patients continued to return to the hospital for psychotherapy, visits to their social workers and medication. Some patients used the hospital's day care program. Several have lived in the hospital's half-way house. Their families also have turned to the hospital for assistance when difficulties arose and several remain in contact with social workers.

One year after discharge, six of the eight patients remained in the community. One patient already mentioned relapsed after three months, was readmitted and remains hospitalized. One patient having a history of post-lobotomy epilepsy died during a grand mal seizure. The others remain unhospitalized and have continued to show improvement. At the end of a year, these patients are still largely not self-supporting, and most continue to use the services of the hospital in various ways. Many, however, have tried several living arrangements before a satisfactory one was reached. The following cases illustrate some of the problems which have come up and some of the present living situations of the patients.

G. C., 43 years old, discharged after 14 years' hospitalization. She worked as a mother's helper for three months, left this job by mutual agreement, though remaining friendly with her employer, and lived with an aunt for three months. Her aunt moved away. The patient took a room in the hospital's halfway house and obtained a job as cleaning woman in an office building. After seven months she moved to a rooming house where she has friends. At present, she has worked steadily for nine months, keeps in touch with her family and engages in a limited number of outside activities. She continues to see her social worker once a week.

H. L., 49 years old, discharged after 13 years' hospitalization. This patient went home to live with her elderly mother and came in once a month to see her social worker for a period of six months. These visits have been discontinued. Both the patient and her mother are supported by Disability Assistance. The patient states that she is glad to have a chance to take care of her mother after the years that her mother looked after her. She has recently joined a lodge.

L. C., 26 years old, was discharged after six years' hospitalization and went back to live at home with her parents. She worked briefly during the Christmas rush. She has continued to use the Day Hospital and to see her social worker once a week. Though she has not made many social contacts outside the home, she has shown an increasing capacity to make successful social relationships in the Day Hospital setting.

223

DISCUSSION

Our study to date suggests that the factors influencing the discharge of chronic schizophrenic patients lie outside the areas of clinical condition and social behavior, once the patient has reached a certain level of adjustment within the hospital. We found the most significant factors to be establishment of a psychotherapeutic relationship with a doctor or social worker and the patient's relationship with his family.

During our study, eight, or one-third, of our patients were discharged, of whom six remained in the community at least one year later. These patients were selected on the basis of their chronicity and were studied because their chances of discharge were minimal under ordinary circumstances. Despite the small size of this sample, these patients were representative of long term schizophrenic reactions.

The failure to effect discharge in two-thirds of this group demonstrates that our treatment program is at best a partial answer to the problem. It is an open question whether a longer treatment period would materially increase our discharge rate.

At the present time, we cannot evaluate the importance of the drugs used in this study. The improvement rate in our patients was comparable to that reported in other drug studies (2, 3). Since improvement was related to discharge in our study, we feel that the use of drugs may have increased the number of patients considered for discharge. The drugs did not appear to be sufficient in themselves to effect discharge. The control group treated for the same length of time at the state hospital showed approximately equal improvement, but had only one discharge out of 22 patients. This will be further discussed in another paper (4).

The effect of the transfer on these patients cannot be fully evaluated. Many patients were upset by the transfer and temporarily showed an aggravation of their symptoms. Later effects of transfer on the discharge rate cannot be separated from the active treatment program since the patients were begun on drugs and other therapies immediately after transfer.

We found that psychotherapy and social casework therapy were related to discharge. This does not mean that chronic patients cannot be discharged without psychotherapy since most chronic patients who leave hospitals have not received such treatment. In our own series, two discharges were due primarily to social work done with the patients' families. The psychotherapy and social casework therapy done in this study took a number of forms. Further study of this aspect of the project is under way, and will be reported later. At this time, the most we can say is that therapy involved the commitment of some one person to the patient over the six month period and after discharge. Other personnel were variously committed to the patients, but their commitments focused primarily on the patient's adjustment within the hospital. Only the doctor and social worker mediate between hospital and community in working toward discharge. Despite the value of other personnel and therapies, patients were not discharged unless a doctor or social worker was actively involved in the discharge planning.

Family involvement was a significant factor in discharging these chronic patients and their chances for discharge frequently depended on whether their families would take them. Since families become reconciled to long term hospitalization, they rarely take steps to get their relatives out of the hospital. In most cases, the hospital must take the initiative in contacting the family and involving them in planning for the patient. This further points up the importance of the role of the psychiatric social worker in treating chronic patients.

Our experience has illustrated the difficulties in discharging a patient whose family is unable or unwilling to take him. That we were able to discharge any such patients was due in part to the availability of the half-way house for women. The lack of a half-way house for men was in part responsible for our failure to discharge male patients. Transitional facilities such as half-way houses are necessary to discharge patients without families.

We have found ourselves having some afterthoughts about the usefulness of an intensive treatment center for chronic patients.

When this study was planned, we naively assumed that an intensive program would be the optimal treatment measure. Our hypothesis was that more treatment would equal better treatment. In fact, we found that this was not necessarily true. Involvement in the milieu did not improve the patient's chances for discharge. We do not mean to suggest that social therapies are not beneficial to the patient within the hospital, but they were not related to the problem of getting the chronic patient out.

There are indications that in some circumstances an intensive treatment program may be too stressful. We have no doubt that all the patients were stressed by the program at the Massachusetts Mental Health Center, and in certain cases felt that the stress was clearly detrimental. Some patients appear to require a more relaxed pace than was provided. It has been suggested that the patients were popped from the deep freeze into the fire. A therapeutic community designed to meet the needs of acute patients may not equally well meet the needs of all chronic patients. Much more investigation is needed before we will know what size treatment units, composition of patient group, type of therapy and number of personnel are needed to work effectively with chronic patients.

This brings us to the question of the value of a treatment program which includes the discharge of disabled people. We have often been asked whether the hospital is not in fact the best place for such people, for their own sake and for the welfare of the community. Thus far, our one year follow-up indicates that the patients continue to show improvement in their appearance and in the extent of their social contacts after discharge. Moreover, the patients were uniformly pleased to be out of the hospital. Not all were satisfied with their present living arrangements but all stated that they preferred to remain in the community.

The effects of these patients on their families is not so clear. We do not know how heavy a burden has been placed on these families or what long-range effects it may have on family life. Upsets have occurred but so far no family has returned their relative to the hospital.

We have no way of judging what effect these patients have on the community at large. Most of the patients we have discharged are currently not self-supporting so that the burden of their support falls upon their families or community agencies. We do not know how much it costs to maintain such a person in the community. On a purely economic basis, it may be less expensive to keep him hospitalized. In terms of his individual welfare it appears better to get a patient out of the hospital.

Our study suggests that discharging a chronic patient involves blurring the traditional boundaries between hospital and community. In all our cases, psychiatric social work and investigation of community agencies began months before a patient was discharged. The hospital continued to work with each patient after discharge so that the treatment program extended into the community. Discharge may be viewed as one step in the treatment program, with therapeutic value of its own.

SUMMARY

Twenty-four chronic schizophrenic patients were treated with tranquilizing drugs, social and psychological therapies for a six month period. Eight patients, or one-third of the group, were discharged. Discharge was related to improvement, but not contingent upon it. The factors influencing discharge were a good hospital adjustment, a psychotherapeutic relationship with a doctor or psychiatric social worker, the attitude of the patient's family and the availability of community resources. Involvement in the milieu therapies (occupational therapy, physical therapy and recreational therapy) was not related to discharge. The treatment program continued after discharge through contacts with the patient's doctor, psychiatric social worker and the hospital facilities. Follow-up studies showed continued improvement after discharge, and the patients themselves expressed a desire to remain in the community. Within the framework of this treatment program, discharge may be viewed as a therapeutic measure in chronic schizophrenia.

ACKNOWLEDGMENT

This investigation was supported by a research grant, MY-1690 (C2) from the National Institute of Mental Health, Public Health Service.

BIBLIOGRAPHY

1. Brooks, G. W.: Experience with the use of chlorpromazine and reserpine in psychiatry. *New Eng. J. Med., 254:* 1119, 1956.

2. Barsa, J. A., and Kline, N. S.: A comparative study of reserpine, chlorpromazine and combined therapy. *A.M.A. Arch. Neurol. Psychiat., 76:* 90, 1956.

3. Barsa, J. A., and Kline, N. S.: Combined reserpine-chlorpromazine in treatment of disturbed psychotics. *A.M.A. Arch. Neurol. Psychiat., 74:* 280, 1955.

4. Bullard, D. M., Jr., Hoffman, B. R., and Havens, L. L.: *The Relative Value of Tranquilizing Drugs and Social and Psychological Therapies in Chronic Schizophrenia.* American Psychiatric Association, Philadelphia, May 1, 1959.

DISCUSSION OF DR. BULLARD'S PAPER

DR. PIERRE DENIKER:—

I appreciate the privilege of being able to make these few remarks. There seems to have been some question as to whether or not the therapeutic community even existed as such; whether we were not really talking about "therapeutic communities." I would agree with the latter, for it seems to me that the kind of therapeutic community will probably depend to a degree on the location, the leader, etc.

In France we have recently formed a research committee, and one of its primary problems will be the study of treatment techniques for the chronic patient. There are a number of chronic patients who can be returned to the community after intensive treatment. One of our major concerns, similar to those expressed by Dr. Bullard, are the social problems in the families of chronic schizophrenic patients. Unfortunately, there are frequently not enough caseworkers available for the necessary studies to be done.

While much has been said about the effects of drugs in calming the agitated patient and consequently bringing tranquility to a whole ward, you may be interested to know that in our wards at St. Anne's in Paris, the reverse has occasionally been true. With the new sulfonamide phenothiazine, many patients become hyperactive, "turbulent," introducing an air of tension. For the first time in at least 10 years (since Professor Delay and I introduced chlorpromazine), some nurses and attendants have actually been somewhat fearful of the patients. This is a curious sidelight on this new drug which we consider to be the most potent phenothiazine available to date.

DISCUSSION OF DR. BULLARD'S PAPER

Dr. Anthony Hordern:—

Following Dr. Bullard's interesting paper, and Dr. Sarwer-Foner's remarks, I would like to make a few observations out of personal experience in the problem of rehabilitating chronic deteriorated schizophrenic patients. Much of this conference has been spent in making references to Dr. Maxwell Jones' therapeutic community at Belmont Hospital, England. However, Dr. Jones' patient community consists mainly of psychopathic personalities, and I would maintain that problems encountered in dealing with chronic schizophrenics are very different. My own interest and experience, therefore, stems from six months working in a locked male ward with 55 patients, mainly chronic schizophrenics, in a large federal hospital. For the 55 patients, one was provided with one nurse and three attendants on the morning shift, together with three attendants and a part-time nurse on the afternoon shift and, to cover the night, two attendants. Dr. Sarwer-Foner referred to Lewis Hill's "Schizophrenic Way of Life." I personally feel that this can be a very dangerous abstraction as a concept of schizophrenia, especially when utilized by nurses and attendants in the absence of much occupational therapy or psychiatric social work. A combination of this intellectual approach and the old custodial attitude can lead, in my experience, to "permissivity"—the patients are allowed to slip into degraded behavior, mannerisms, stereotypies, and neglect of their personal appearance and habits. In time patients become bored, apathetic and drowsy; then, as frustration increases, they become hostile—they fight explosively from time to time requiring ever larger doses of drugs for their control. An idea seems to have grown up in some hospitals that it is therapeutic to leave the patient alone until he is able to help himself—since schizophrenia is conceived as an extreme "defense measure," it is felt that the appropriate therapeutic approach is not to disturb the patient until he feels "safe enough" to relinquish his schizophrenic defense. However, one must remember that schizophrenic impairment of volition implies that the patient seldom has much incentive to help himself, and the ward environment, if it provides few privileges and no pay for work, however hard he may try, likewise does not provide many incentives for improvement. The patient finds in many hospitals that he has to depend on charity for even such slight necessities as candy and cigarettes.

In view of the present staffing situation with which we are confronted, it seems to me that the only solution to the general problem, is giving patients the push and attention they require to organize them into groups of 10 or 15 members which operate autonomously. Permanent attendants are then assigned to each group whose consistent attitudes facilitate and promote patient identification with their behavior. The allocation of patients into groups can be made according to their self-sufficiency and adjustment level. One or two reliable patients can be provided to help with their more deteriorated companions, and the physician and nurse can then work with the patients through the attendant. It is necessary to provide weekly meetings for patients and nursing personnel, and also subsequent weekly meetings for the nursing personnel involved. Good results in our cases were quite rapidly achieved—after three months, of 55 patients, 35 could be allowed off the ward instead of five, and 10 were able to work off the ward instead of two. The cost of drugs per patient per day fell from 19 to 13 cents, fighting diminished, and seclusion became very seldom necessary. Had we not been in the position of having to accept acutely disturbed patients from open wards from time to time, it would no doubt have been possible to open the ward door.

However, I would like to stress that there is nothing very new in this sort of approach—it was popularized by Myerson 20 years ago, and also by Rees, whose methods have been described by Symona. But their work too was not new—it was a structural application of Bleuler's therapeutic philosophy, a philosophy founded, as Zilboorg and Krapf have pointed out, on his experience at Rhinau in the 1890's before he took the chair of Psychiatry at Zurich. Bleuler emphasized that no patient was ever to be completely given up, and that inappropriate behavior was not be to tolerated. It was not, he thought, in the patient's best interest to be allowed to act in a degraded or senseless fashion. Bleuler brought community resources into Rhinau, and he was indeed transforming the hospital into a Therapeutic Community like Gheel, before he went to Zurich in 1898. Hermann Simon, at Gutersloh in 1927, popularized occupational therapy, and had ideas similar to these of Bleuler. Simon stressed the idea of the responsibility of the sick patient for his behavior during the illness, and also the responsibility of the doctor, nurses and attendants to the patient in this regard. Since attendants often come from socio-economic backgrounds which resemble those of patients, Simon saw the value of employing them to treat patients, a resource we probably do not effectively utilize even today. Bleuler, Simon, and others like them, including Myerson and Rees, saw the value of preventing faulty habits and the importance of encouraging healthy patterns of behavior, an approach that was also emphasized by Adolph Meyer.

In our ward, for more severely deteriorated patients, habit training of a simple nature was necessary. The patients were trained to take care of each other's appearance in a suitable fashion, and to behave appropriately. This was found to increase self-interest, and improve morale. As has been the experience in Britain over the last few years, we have found that the improvement the patients have shown has provoked increased interest by relatives. One feels that this is important, since Dr. Bullard's paper has stressed that while his patients at the Massachusetts Mental Health Center and his patients in the state hospital both improved to the same extent as the result of his therapeutic program, those in the Health Center were discharged much more frequently through increased social work and greater family interest. Accordingly, everything we can do to get the relatives of these deteriorated patients interested is of value. It seems that the prognosis is much better than formerly, for some of the improvement that can be elicited by habit training can be "held" by ataractic drugs. There seem to be some kind of synergistic effect between drugs and an active therapeutic environment.

DISCUSSION OF DR. BULLARD'S PAPER

Dr. Max Fink:—

These observations of Dr. Bullard and Mrs. Hoffman are indeed remarkable because they demonstrate quite clearly that the initial expectations that phrenotropic agents might be equivalent of Ehrlich's "Magic Bullet" are unfounded. Apparently, the transfer of patients from the chronic wards to a more active service was helpful in permitting the patients to behave in a fashion more acceptable to the therapeutic staff and to consider two-thirds for discharge. What is crucial, however, is that of the patients considered for discharge only half could be separated from the hospital because only half had an outside environment ready and willing to accept them. This discussion emphasizes, I believe, the need for a unified approach to the treatment of these patients. Unified, in the concept that the treatment phase in the hospital, with its attendant emphasis on psychotherapy, group therapy, chemotherapy, etc., is but one phase of the treatment process. Equally important is the preparation of the community for the individual.

I have a number of questions. I would be interested in knowing whether the patients who were discharged showed any differences from those who were not with regards to the F scale and other social factors; also, on a hospital adjustment continuum, was there any difference between the discharged and the not discharged groups? By hospital adjustment continuum, I mean were the patients who had adjusted to the chronic institution in terms of work relationship any different than those who had failed to establish such a work relationship. Finally, did I understand that the control patients not transferred to the Massachusetts Mental Health Center also improved at the rate of one-third? If so, was this a discharge rate or a psychiatric improvement rating? If the latter, I wonder how much of the psychiatrist's expectations entered into this judgment.

REPLY BY DR. BULLARD:—

In reply to Dr. Fink's first question, the patients' hospital adjustment was not related to discharge once they had reached a successful open ward adjustment. In the open ward group, holding a hospital job occurred no more frequently in the discharged than the non-discharged patients.

Discharge rates and improvement rates were listed separately. The improvement rates were the same in the control group and the group discussed in the present paper. Ratings of psychiatric improvement were compared with ratings made independently by a social psychologist and ward personnel. There was substantial agreement in all but two of these cases.

DISCUSSION OF DR. BULLARD'S PAPER

DR. H. PETER LAQUEUR:—

The difficulty to make schizophrenic patients "wish to return to life" outside the confining but also sheltering conditions in a mental hospital are well known. We have used in our ward discussions the term *"point of no return"* rather than Hill's term "the schizophrenic compromise" in order to indicate that for each patient there exists a certain "flexibility" (as to when the "point of no return" is reached).

233

Since the "point of no return" psychologically depends on a) the patients inner situation (strength or illness) and b) the pressures of the external world which he tries to avoid, we can direct the treatment in our therapeutic community towards a change in both factors. We build up the patient's inner strength and capacity to cope with stress. We can enable him to deal with external stress better through group and family therapy which increases his social perceptiveness of the needs of his environment and with individual therapy which deepens his insight.

WORK AND FAMILY ADJUSTMENT
OF MENTAL PATIENTS UPON
THEIR RETURN TO THE COMMUNITY

Else B. Kris, M.A., M.D.

INTRODUCTION

When attempting to implement some concepts of the therapeutic milieu in a clinic setting providing aftercare services for patients returned to the community, it is imperative to keep in mind particular problems they must face. It seems important to recall that mental patients permitted to leave the hospital are expected to adjust in the community. While methods of psychiatric treatment are steadily changing and the importance of work as an integral part of therapy becomes more and more recognized, there are still great needs to be met in order to assist those leaving the hospitals in their striving for socio-economic rehabilitation.

It has been stated that schizophrenic patients have considerable difficulties in adjusting to social and economic life after hospitalization. The possibilities for rehabilitation of some individuals returning to the community are generally considered to be poor, particularly where the illness was of long duration or after prolonged hospital stay.

It was further presumed that unfavorable family constellations can not only impede community reintegration but predispose to a recurrence of psychotic symptoms. Previous experience indicated that many psychiatric patients when exposed to severe pressure at work would respond with a reactivation of symptoms, and that being discharged from a job could contribute to renewed psychotic breakdown.

METHOD

One hundred patients were closely observed from the day following their release from the hospital. Fifty were admitted during the first year (Group A), and 50 (Group B) at the beginning of the second year.

They were seen weekly during the first two or three months and when necessary more often; the time interval was lengthened later in the study. At the same time close contact was maintained with the family or friends wherever possible.

From the very first interview, the entire research staff tried to impress on each individual that the patient and staff were one group, with a common goal, doing everything possible to facilitate rehabilitation of the patient and readjustment in the community. Relatives and friends were likewise instructed and advised to bring any problems to the staff's immediate attention.

Patients were seen at first individually by one or the other member of the research staff. Plans for their future, possibilities of employment and various problems were discussed. Pains were taken to avoid exerting any pressure, particularly with regard to work. Whenever the wish was expressed to venture out to secure employment without assistance, this was agreed upon. At the same time the individual was assured that assistance would be available if so requested.

The research staff consisted initially of psychiatrists, a psychologist, social workers, and later a vocational counselor, occupational therapist and nurse. Meetings were held at least once a week, and frequently such sessions had to be repeated daily. As the study progressed, patients were asked to take part in sessions where their individual problems were to be discussed. It was soon learned that they resented these group sessions, where, as one stated, "I feel like being taken to staff conference and I get scared. It reminds me too much of the hospital and I want to forget this." Thereafter it was tried to see patients in groups who were confronted by problems of a similar nature. While some benefits seemed to be derived from these sessions, it soon became apparent that most of the patients attended mainly because they felt obliged, did not like these sessions and insisted on being seen individually.

Gradually, as the study proceeded, it became necessary to include the clerical personnel in these staff meetings, as patients were frequently in telephone contact with them or in personal contact while waiting at the time of visit.

It was noted that any change of personnel, whether clerical or professional, caused noticeable uneasiness on the part of patients. The same applied when one or the other member of staff went on vacation and the patient had to be seen by another person.

238

As dealing with former mental patients and their particular needs presented a fairly new experience for the vocational counselor, the value of having him join the staff conference became apparent. At the end of the first year and during the second year, he felt more at ease, and became more confident in dealing with mental patients. He agreed that the experience had made it much easier to understand their particular rehabilitation needs.

On occasions, a particular patient felt more comfortable when seen by the same social worker or psychiatrist and not shifted from one to another. In such cases, the patient chose the staff member he felt most comfortable with; the interview findings were then discussed generally in the regular staff meetings. Any staff sensitivities arising from such choice were discussed at the conference and cleared as far as possible. This became necessary after we observed that unresolved sensitivities had a damaging effect on the patient's progress. During these conferences, plans for a specific approach to each individual patient were minutely discussed to assure as far as possible unanimous handling of any question that might arise. Individualization of the patient's various needs and resolution of most staff friction made patients feel as members of a group in which all forces tended to work together for their benefit. They gradually realized that they no longer had to face difficulties alone, and could rely upon us for help. As a result, they gradually became more self-confident and self-reliant.

RESULTS

The overall findings during the first two years of this study seemed to indicate that this approach is fruitful. One of the most striking findings was that more patients than generally expected were able to find employment on their own initiative, without assistance. In several cases where rehabilitation services were offered and at first accepted, the patients later decided to find employment on their own rather than go through a period of training. A considerable number were successful in these endeavors. It was further observed that many patients remained on their first job for one year or longer. However, several changed from job to job on their own volition, without assistance.

Group A:— Fourteen patients were found to require help from the Division of Vocational Rehabilitation. Twenty found employment on their own (one of whom was subsequently returned to the hospital), and nine worked as homemakers. Five (10%) were considered to be unemployable, and two of these were eventually rehospitalized. At the end of the first year, a total of three patients (6%) were rehospitalized. At the end of the second year, four additional patients (8%) were rehospitalized.

Group B:— Twelve patients became homemakers upon their return to the community; 23 found employment at the end of the year without assistance, and only one was considered unemployable. Four patients were returned to the hospital during this time, and 11 were referred to the Division of Vocational Rehabilitation. Of the 20 patients who were referred for rehabilitation services, 10 are listed as presently employed with future plans for retraining. At the end of the first year, four patients (8%) were rehospitalized.

Of the 72% of patients in Group A who showed unsatisfactory social and family adjustment during the first year, 26% showed considerable improvement in this area during the second year as they felt at ease in the community and in their personal life in general. In several cases, this improvement seemed related to steady employment. As they became more secure in their job, they also gained confidence and self-respect, as reflected by the attitudes of family, neighbors and friends.

It seemed in general that a husband or wife readjusted better than daughter, son, or siblings in a family. In several instances, it was felt that if patients would be moved away from their homes, not only would their general adjustment be improved, but their social reorientation would have benefited considerably as well.

For the remainder of the study it is planned, while continuing to keep Groups A and B under observation, to admit a third group, "C", comprising 50 patients and to study them in an analagous manner.

240

The following case reports illustrate some of the problems encountered, as well as some of the ways by which their solution was attempted.

Case 1: When Miss M. A. returned home after 11 years of hospital residence her rather domineering mother had arranged for the patient to start working immediately at the factory where she, herself, was employed. It took several sessions with the patient before learning that she had worked at secretarial jobs before admission to the hospital, that she disliked the factory work, and considered it degrading. At the same time she fully realized, that having been away for so many years, she would require retraining before being able to compete in the job market. Because of her generally poor personal appearance, a tendency to withdrawal and difficulty in establishing interpersonal contacts, several staff members considered her employability as a white collar worker remote and, therefore, felt any plans for retraining unwarranted. However, it was agreed to make a trial effort. In preparation, all attention was concentrated on getting her better and properly fitted clothes, teaching her how to use make-up, while at the same time attempting to overcome her mother's resistance to this program. The latter preferred to have her daughter the way she was, working at her side in the factory under supervision every minute of the day. As the patient's personal appearance improved, she gained more confidence in herself, established better contact with the various members of the research staff and her outlook on life became more hopeful and positive. After several months, during which she had continued with her factory work to the satisfaction of her supervisors, arrangements were made to attend evening classes at a business school. She completed this course very successfully, withstood the strain of working while attending school, and is now awaiting job placement. Her teachers consider the outlook as very good.

Case 2: R. T., a 21 year old girl, had done factory work prior to being hospitalized for one year. Returned home, her parents insisted she take occupational training. The staff agreed upon her placement in a workshop for evaluation of any special abilities. After several days, she was taught to operate a sewing machine. She became increasingly tense and upset, and stated that she did not like this work. The shop supervisors, with whom the clinic staff discussed the matter, blamed the difficulties on the patient's deficient vision, and she was fitted with eye glasses. However, the anxiety persisted, becoming worse as she became disturbed and complained of auditory hallucinations. She was particularly restless at night. The workshop supervisors continued to insist that this was the right type of work and that she should stay with it. As she became more difficult to manage at home, her parents finally were persuaded to part with the idea of special training, which had meant status and prestige to them. Thus, her workshop attendance was terminated. Having felt that the clinic staff had not helped her, but had rather caused her trouble, she became resentful and was very reluctant to continue her visits. It took considerable effort to reestablish a good relationship between the patient and staff. Gradually, as this was achieved, the overt psychotic manifestations subsided. Finally new plans could be worked out. She made it clear that she enjoyed helping her mother in the household, cooking, cleaning and shopping. A few months later she ventured out on her own and accepted a household job in her immediate neighborhood. One year later she is working well, is happy, shows good insight, and is free of any psychotic symptoms. The relationship with her parents, for sometime extremely strained, is now free of friction and tension. She has made new friends in her own peer group and takes part in their various social activities.

Case 3: A. A., a 29 year old male, following his release after 10 years of hospital residence, wanted to become an auto mechanic. He was placed in a training school and completed the course with fair grades. With assistance from the school he secured employment, but after one day at work left in a state of panic. His father was very angry and expressed open hostility, calling him "plain lazy" and "just no good." The patient became tense, fearful, and began to respond to auditory hallucinations. Under drug therapy, these symptoms were controlled. He would only consult the clinic psychiatrist, refusing to see other staff members. After several weeks, he began to work in his house and about the garden. Finally he started to look for odd jobs, which he managed to find and did well. After numerous sessions, the parents began to understand the situation better. As the tension at home diminished, the patient showed better adjustment and, without assistance, secured part-time employment in a grocery store. He has maintained this job for the past eight months, has begun to make friends, to take part in church and other social activities.

CONCLUSION

During a special study conducted over the past two years, it appeared that some of the principles of the therapeutic community can be successfully put to use in an aftercare clinic. Patients released from prolonged hospital residence were helped to regain a social and economic place in daily life. With individualized attention, a considerable percentage was able to find employment, many of them becoming self-supporting. The number of returns to the hospital was kept comparatively low.

ACKNOWLEDGMENT

This study was carried out under a special grant from the Office of Vocational Rehabilitation, Department of Health, Education, and Welfare, Washington, D. C.

SUMMARY OF THE DISCUSSION

The interchange of ideas during the meeting was fruitful, spirited and provocative, giving rise to some concrete feelings regarding the therapeutic community. An exact definition of this concept was not attempted, but emphasis was laid on defining its parameters, goals and limitations. It became obvious that generalizations and extensions of the idea, as originally conceived by Sir Maxwell Jones in Belmont working with a population of psychopaths and social deviants, was not possible. The therapeutic community as such was not considered the chief therapeutic endeavor but complementary to specific measures directed at each patient. Restructuring of the environment—i. e., open door, day and night hospital, etc., could be viewed as making it more therapeutic while the more specific treatments—drugs, psychotherapy, ECT, insulin and others—were employed.

Manipulation of environmental social factors must, of necessity, vary depending on a) the setting, b) the group leader, and c) the staff. Complete permissiveness could hardly be indicated in a unit treating psychopaths, for here this would almost constitute an unconscious acknowledgement of their anti-social behavior. There was much discussion concerning "the door"—must it be opened or closed? Here, opinion was divided and the consensus was best epitomized by the statement of Greenblatt and Levinson, "An open door does not necessarily mean an open mind."

The necessity of group meetings with full participation of staff and patients, the need for open lines of communication within the staff, and between staff and patients was repeatedly stressed. While some groups met daily, the frequency of such meetings would seem to depend upon the patient population. The staff working in a therapeutic community must have a mutual respect one for the other, be able to discuss freely all problems, and possess the ability to compromise where opinions were sharply divided. The importance of recognizing unconscious influences upon selection of patients for particular treatments was discussed. The type of treatment could be psychotherapeutic, chemotherapeutic or physiologic alone or combined, but not as a unique method for all patients.

The group leader was seen as the driving force behind the therapeutic community, imparting much of his own personality to the operation. Some felt that historically the demise of such liberalized wards could be traced to the departure of the leader without being replaced.

A great deal of attention was given to the difficulties encountered by various therapeutic communities as they began operation. High level support, both from central and local sources, was deemed essential to a successful operation. In most state hospitals they represented a radical departure from accustomed practices and, as such, were bound to generate much anxiety elsewhere in the institution. While it was believed that every effort should be made to relate such a ward to the rest of the hospital, no ready solution of these problems were found.

The work therapy program extensively used in Europe received some discussion but, with one exception, has not been used much in this country. The importance of the final stages of treatment— the patient's rehabilitation and re-entrance into the community life was examined by several speakers. The paucity of facilities was noted both in this country and abroad. Unless adequate community resources were developed with an extensive rehabilitation program and follow-up psychiatric care, there would be little possibility of separating chronic schizophrenic patients from the hospital.

Perhaps a quotation from the cover of the March 1959 issue of Mental Hospitals might best epitomize the meeting, "Men are never so likely to settle a question rightly as when they discuss it freely."

INDEX

247

Alper, B. S., 16
Anxiety, effect of drug therapy for in animals, 38
Apprehension, effect of drug therapy for in animals, 38
Atkins, J., 161

B

Babikian, H., 72, 77
Bacon, Francis, 7
Baerends, G. P., 42
Baerends-van Roon, J. M., 42
Barrabee, P. S., 208
Barsa, J. A., 228
Beard, G. M., 5
Bell, G. M., 124
Bleuler, E., 231
Boag, T. J., 163, 173
Bond, Earl D., 5, 13, 15
Borstal system, 11-13
  characteristics of, 11
  history of, 11
Bowlby, J., 42
Boyd, R. W., 208
Brennan, Edward, 207
Brill, Henry, 3, 16, 208
Brooks, George W., 19, 217, 228
Brown, E. L., 100, 124, 208
Briggs, D. L., 72, 77
Brody, E. B., 55
Bullard, Dexter M., Jr., 207, 215, 228, 229, 231, 232, 233
Butler, S., 7

C

Cameron, D. D., 122, 125
Cameron, D. E., 173
Cameron, J. D., 55
Carmichael, William, 207
Carpenter, C. R., 41
Carstairs, G. M., 161
Caudill, W., 55
Chance, M. R. A., 42
Charatan, F. B., 76, 77, 125
Chassel, J., 188
Chiarugi, V., 5, 8

Chittick, R. A., 19
Chlorpromazine
  attitude of nurses toward use of, 198
  effect of on activity of Rhesus monkeys, 33-34
  introduced by Dr. Deniker, 229
  use for apprehension-anxiety in animals, 38
  use in study of chronic schizophrenics, 217
  use to overcome resistance in animals, 39
Cohen, R. A., 161
Collias, N. E., 31, 41
Colp, Ralph, Jr., 207
Conolly, J., 5, 9
Contagious behavior
  defined, 40
  effect of drug therapy on in animals, 39-40
  in schools of fish, 39-40
  use of with goals, 40
Cordeau, Mrs. F., 96
Cousineau, A., 96
Cummings, E., 76, 209
Cummings, J., 76, 209

D

Dahlestrom, W. G., 146
Dancey, T. E., 79, 85
Daniels, M. L., 161
Daquin, J., 8
Darling, F. F., 42
Deane, W. N., 19
Delay, J., 229
Delgado, J., 33, 42
D'Elia, F., 162
Denber, Herman C. B., 57, 76, 77, 125, 127, 128
Deniker, Pierre, 228
Denny, R., 209
Deutsch, A., 16
Devereux, G., 55
Dickens, Charles, 121, 125
Dix, Dorothea Linde, 5, 9, 11
Donnelly, J., 209
Drug therapy
  and open door policy, 206

and the therapeutic community, 204-206

conflict in psychiatrist toward, 211

difficulties with anti-depressant drugs, 51-52

drug-personality-environment interaction, 40

effects of on aggressive behavior, 35-37

effects of on apprehension-anxiety, 38

effects of on behavioral processes, 33-40

    locomotor activity, 33

effects of on hospital atmosphere, 193

effects of on locomotor activity, 33-35

effects of on sexual behavior, 37-38

factors in referral of patients for, 213

hyperactivity induced by, 229

importance of in chronic schizophrenia, 224

in mental hospitals, 191-207

interviews with staff regarding, 196

motivation of referral for, 205

objectives of, 33

personal value orientations of staff and, 212

reaction to sulfonamide phenothiazine, 229

relation of social status of patient and staff toward, 210-211

relationship between social class of psychiatrist and attitude toward, 210

relationship of need for to ward atmosphere, 204-205

responses to anti-depressant drugs, 51-52

    aggressive over-activity, 52

    defensive hostility, 52

social distance between patient and psychiatrist and, 211-212

study of use at Massachusetts Mental Health Center, 191-207, See also Massachusetts Mental Health Center

use as alternate to psychotherapy, 213

use of, 204

use of trifluperazine, 52, See also Trifluperazine

use to modify social behavior in animals, 29-40

    contagious behavior, 39-40

    effects of change on stress response, 38

    effects of chlorpromazine on Rhesus monkeys, 33

    effects of methamphetamine on Charles River rats, 34-35

    effects of on aggressive behavior, 35-37

    effects of on apprehension-anxiety, 38

    effects of on locomotor activity, 33-35

    effects of tranquilization on aggressive behavior in rats, 35, 36

    effects of tranquilizer on defensive response, 36

    group interaction and toxicity of drugs, 34-35

    imprinting, 38-39

    interaction effect on locomotor activity of rats, 34

    role of defensive response, 36

    use of tranquilizers for apprehension-anxiety, 38

Duckman, J., 161

E

Edam, Irwin, 16

Ehrlich, J., 232

Eisen, S. B., 209

Eldred, Donald, 21

Emerson, A. E., 42

Emlen, J. T., Jr., 41

Erich, I., 209

F

Fabricius, E., 42

Feldman, P. E., 209

Felix, R. H., 120, 125

Fink, Max, 149, 162, 213, 232, 233

Flynn, Ruth, 124

Freud, Sigmund, 155, 161

251

Lipsitt, Don R., 43
Locomotion, effect of drug therapy on in animals, 33-35

M

MacDonald, J. M., 161
MacIver, J., 173, 209, 212
Maclay, W. S., 120, 125
MacMillan, D., 122, 124
Mandelbrote, B., 77, 119, 125
Manhattan State Hospital
  conclusions of study of therapeutic community, 75
  description of ward after research began, 62-64
    attention to personal hygiene and dress, 63
    celebration of patient birthdays, 63
    change of clothing of patients, 63
    changes in furnishing of ward, 62
    closer relationships with non-medical personnel, 64
    extra-mural outings, 63
    new role of nurses, 63-64
    new status of nurses, 64
    participation of patients, 63
    patient-personnel meetings, 62-63
    use of suggestion box, 63
    work of patients, 63
  description of ward prior to study, 60-62
    ages of patients, 61
    diagnostic categories, 61
    duration of hospitalization, 62
  group meetings, 67-69
    as mirror of staff indecision, 68
    participation of patients in, 67
    reaction of patients in, 67
    response to patients' suggestions, 69
    results of meetings, 68
    use of notes in suggestion box for discussion, 68
  observations of therapeutic community, 70-75
    administrative procedures, 74
    application of social approach, 75
    benefits of, 74-75
    conduct of and along psychodynamic principles, 74
    discipline problems on ward, 71-72
    effect of indecision, 74
    feasibility of therapeutic community, 70
    generalizations between cultures, 73
    necessity of open door for therapeutic community, 72
    need for oral gratification, 71
    needs of patients, 71
    patients not candidates for therapeutic community, 71
    qualifications for leader of, 74
    problem of personnel shortage, 70-71
    problem of sexual promiscuity, 72
    social therapy versus chemotherapy, 72, 73
    staff problems, 73
    treatment used, 73
  physician's attitudes, 69-70
    discord among physicians, 70
    problems of ward, 70
    the ward as a part of the hospital, 70
  results of research study, 64-67
    acceptance of new patients by old patients, 64-65
    changes in atmosphere of ward, 65
    changes in patients, 64
    changes in physical setting, 64
    number patients placed on convalescent care, 66, 67
    number patients placed on discharge status, 66, 67
    open door policy, 65, 66
    plateau of activity of patients, 65
    removal of bars from windows, 65
    results of social service work, 66

256

research on chronic patients in France, 228

results of anxiety in patients with, 50

social needs of people with, 81

Mental patients discharged from hospital

attendance of patients at conferences, 238

attitude of staff in study, 237-238

effect of unfavorable family constellations on, 237

importance of unresolved sensitivities of staff, 239

inclusion of clerical staff in conferences with, 238

individualization of patient needs, 239

interviews with, 237, 238

patient's choice of therapist, 239

problems faced upon discharge, 237

prognosis for rehabilitation, 237

research staff conducting study of, 238

response of patients to individualized approach, 239

response to pressure at work, 237

results of study of, 239-243

    adjustment according to status in family, 240

    case report illustrations of problems encountered, 241-243

    initiative of patients, 239

    job stability of patients, 239-240

    social and family adjustment, 240

value of vocational counselor, 239

work and family adjustment of upon return to community, 235-243

Meprobamate, use to inhibit imprinting in Mallard ducks, 39

Meszaros, A. F., 45, 55, 208, 214

Methamphetamine

effect on activity of Charles River rats, 34-35

use to promote aggressiveness, 36

Meyer, Adolph, 231

Mohr, G. J., 161

Moore, Kenneth B., 27

Moore, Robert, 207

Moore, Thomas, 7

Morter, R. A., 16

Murchison, C., 41

Myerson, A., 231

N

Neiman, G., 96

Nurses

attitude of toward use of chlorpromazine, 198

attitudes toward open door, 114-115, 116-117

attitudes toward therapeutic community, 69

attitudes toward drug therapy, 198, 200

characteristics of charge nurses, 78

conflict with in nurses regarding role in group meetings, 141

difficulty of therapeutic community on nurses of authoritarian type, 141

duties of in therapeutic community, 91

function of charge nurse, 78

importance of attitudes in therapeutic community, 90

influence of ward nurses, 203

new role on open ward, 63-64

response to ward changes, 69

O

Occupational therapist

attitude of towards drug therapy, 200

role of in day hospital, 170

role of on treatment team, 92

use of in therapeutic community, 183

O'Connor, W., 161

Ogle, W., 79

O'Neill, F. J., 125

Open door policy, 97-124

achieving ideal staff-patient relationships after, 123

as pseudo-freedom, 127

as symbol of advancement of, 124

as treatment fetish, 126

at Manhattan State Hospital, 65, 66

at Massachusetts Mental Health Center
    development of open door in, 100
    escapes from open door unit, 113-114
    final staff discussion prior to opening door, 110
    first experiment of opening last door, 101-105
    patient government and challenge of open door, 107-108
    prelude to second experiment of open door, 105-107
    problem of last closed door, 101
    proceedings of open door committee, 108-110
    response to open door, 111
    situation two years after open door, 117-119
    staff attitudes after door was opened, 116-117
    staff attitudes before open door, 114-116
    staff discussions following open door, 111-113
    survey of attitudes before and after open door, 114
attitude of female patients to, 122
caution in isolated use of, 126
criteria for, 86
desire of patients to continue with, 123
early use of, 10
hospital-community relationships and, 123
in America, 120
meaning of to patients, 126
necessity of for therapeutic community, 72
planning for by patients as therapy, 127
principle of, 126
relation between administration and ward staff in policy changes, 120-121
    conditions to be met in making changes, 121

participation of staff in planning changes, 120-121
trend toward, 119-120
use of committee to study, 110
use of in England, 120
work of staff with patients adapting to new freedoms, 122
Orendenker, Sylvia, 124

P

Patton, J. D., 160
Patton, R. E., 208
Perphenazine
    effect of on aggressive behavior in rats, 35, 36
    use for apprehension-anxiety in animals, 38
    use to overcome resistance in animals, 39
Perrin, George, 207
Pinel, P., 5, 8
Plato, 7, 8, 16
Pollack, B., 55, 208, 210, 211, 212, 213, 214
Pollack, Max, 210
Pollak, O., 76
Pratt, Joseph H., 147, 149
Psychiatrist
    attitudes of patient toward in therapeutic community, 188-189
    attitudes of toward director of therapeutic community, 90
    attitudes of toward drug therapy, 197-198
    attitudes of toward mental hospitals, 158
    attitudes of toward open door policy, 69-70, 114-115
    conflict in toward drug therapy, 211
    duties of in therapeutic community, 91
    feelings regarding status and use of drug therapy, 200
    reluctance to use drug therapy, 196
    role of to therapeutic community, 158
    social distance between patient and, 211-212

S

Sabshin, M., 56, 205, 209

Saint Anne's Hospital Therapeutic Community

attitude and relationship of staff at, 85

attitude toward patients in, 86

composition of treatment team, 89-92

    attitude of staff physicians toward director, 90

    duties of social worker, 91-92

    duties of staff nurses, 91

    duties of staff physicians, 91

    effect of good director on unit, 91

    importance of attitudes of nurses, 90

    importance of director, 89-90

    influence of attitudes of director on staff, 90

    psychologists as a part of, 91

    role of occupational therapist, 92

    size of unit related to attitudes, 90-91

criteria for open unit, 86

expectations of patient's behavior, 87

lines of authority and communication, 84-85

organization of women's unit, 85-87

physical aspects of unit, 82-83

physical organization, 88-89

    day room, 89

    of ward, 83

    patient rooms, 89

    recreational and occupational facilities, 89

    staff offices, 88-89

privileges of patients, 86-87

regulations for patients, 86-87

staff conferences, 85

structure of ward, 87-88

    ages of patients, 88

    goal of treatment, 88

    nurse-patient ratio, 87

    occupations of patients, 88

    sociological context of patients, 88

    symptoms of patients on admission, 87

treatment time, 88

teaching and conferences, 92-93

    handling emergencies, 92-93

    use of conferences with consultant, 92

treatment program, 93-94

    acceptance of patients, 93

    admission orientation, 93

    psychotherapy sessions, 93

    purpose of group therapy, 94

    use of chemotherapy, 93

    use of group therapy, 93-94

    use of psychotherapy, 93

    use of staff conferences, 85

    use of unit to foster self-development of patient, 94

Sarwer-Foner, G. J., 79, 229

Schacht, M., 161

Scheidy, S. F., 42

Scher, J. M., 72, 77

Schizophrenia

allocation of patients into groups, 230

attitudes of female patients toward open door, 122

attitudes of patients toward discharge, 226

case illustrations of discharged patients, 223

change of patients with "permissivity," 229-230

correlation between contact with doctor, social worker and discharge, 219-220

correlation of discharged patients to sex, 222

cost of drugs for, 230

cost to community of discharged patients, 227

dangers of "permissivity," 229-230

disability of group studies; 217-218

discharge plans of patients, 221-222

effect of discharged patients on community, 227

effect of discharge of disabled patients on families, 226

effect of drug therapy on patients with, 51

effect of transfer of patients, 224

evaluation after study of patients with, 219
    clinical condition, 219
    hospital milieu and treatment given, 219
    participation in hospital milieu and discharge, 219

factors influencing discharge of chronic patients with, 215-227

factors in selection of patients for psychotherapy, 221

family involvement as factor in discharge, 225

family placement as factor in discharge of patients, 221-222

follow-up of discharged patients, 223

improvement following discharge, 226

importance of hospital following discharge, 222

importance of treatment program to discharge of, 224

leaving patient alone, 230

method of study of, 217-218

need for caseworkers for studies regarding, 228

need for half way house for men with, 225

need for incentive for improvement, 230

need to study social problems in families of patients, 228

problems of patient with authority, 127

reaction to new environment, 137

relationship of psychotherapy and social casework to, 225

results of psychotherapy with, 225

results of social casework with, 225

results of study of, 218

selection of patients for psychotherapy or social casework, 220-221

study of at Metropolitan State Hospital, 217

timing of decision by patient, 43

use of groups for treatment of, 230

use of half way house for women with, 225

use of intensive treatment program, 225-226

use of work discharge in study of, 218

weekly meetings of patients and nursing personnel, 230

weekly staff meetings, 230

Schjelderup-Ebbe, T., 41

Schlosser, J. R., 59, 76, 77

Schwartz, M. S., 55, 76, 205, 209

Scott, D., 122, 125

Scott, J. P., 41, 42, 43

Sexual behavior, effect of drugs on in animals, 37-38

Sharaf, M. R., 200

Siegal, Fay, 124

Silverberg, W. V., 160

Simmel, E., 187

Simon, Hermann, 231

Slavikova, Cecelia, 124

Sloyd, 10

Smith, C. Conway, 92, 173

Snow, H. B., 119, 125

Social organization of animals
    biological factors in, 31
    cooperative behavior, 32-33
        group interaction, 32
    defined, 31
    dominance hierarchies, 31-32
        displaced aggression, 32
        in chickens, 31
    objectives of drug therapy, 33
        control of aggressive-destructive behavior, 33

Social organization in man
    cooperative behavior, 32-33
        basic components of group interaction, 32
    dominance hierarchies, 31-32
        displaced aggression, 32
        shifts in dominance ranks, 31-32
        social hierarchy, 31
    method of modifying behavior with drugs, 40
    objectives of drug therapy, 33
    timing of learning behavior, 43
    use of tranquilizers for aggressive groups, 36

262